Organize Your Life

Skills You Need to **Conquer** the Areas of **Chaos** in Your Life

Helen Ward Day

BELLA LUNA
PRODUCTIONS

2022

Bella Luna Productions, LLC

Using a Digital Workbook

If you are reading this on a Kindle™, I want you to get as much out of it as possible.

Since you obviously cannot take notes with a pen or pencil on your e-reader's screen, learn how to put notes in via your reading device.

On Kindle™ Cloud Reader and a PC, it's easy. Highlight a spot on the page where you want to add your comment, and you will see two options appear: Highlight and Note. If you choose the note option, a text box will appear where you can enter your answer.

In cases where you find a multiple-choice option, you can use the Highlight function to indicate your choices.

This works very much the same with my Paperwhite.

If you are using another type of e-reader, just do a quick online search for how to add notes!

Granted, this is not as useful as putting down your thoughts where they can be reviewed as you flip through paper pages, but it is a good work around. I hope you find the activities within these pages helpful.

Table of Contents

Introduction:

If you want specific advice on precisely how to organize a closet, my book, *Organize Your Life! Skills You Need to Conquer the Areas of Chaos in Your Life*, will only be marginally helpful. If you are hoping to learn **how to think** about your clothes, your wardrobe and your closet in a way that will help you first organize this area of your life and then maintain the system you develop, this book is for you.

By focusing on thinking skills, this book will allow you to adapt an organization style that will fit your lifestyle, whether it is one of luxurious self-indulgence or Spartan-like simplicity. Hopefully your life will yield fulfilling characteristics of both: simplicity in areas where simplicity fosters your creative energies, and decadent luxury in areas when your life needs a little TLC.

This workbook is designed to walk you through organizing areas of your life, in concrete, finite chunks. You may have two or ten areas that need attention, but focusing on five as a maximum number is best. After you've mastered your thinking about organizing, you can tackle more. Right now, we want to focus on doing a limited thing very well, not tackling a huge project and doing it badly. Quality counts.

Get started today on improving your life from the inside out.

Before We Begin: Organization Self Quiz [Circle Answer]

	Completely Disagree	Somewhat Disagree	Somewhat Agree	Completely Agree
Overall Organization				
I am well organized.				
	(1)	2	3	4
I seldom have to look for things I misplace.				
	(1)	2	3	4
My work role is enhanced by my level of organization.				
	1	2	(3)	4
I do not procrastinate at work.				
	1	(2)	3	4
I have high standards, but I am not a perfectionist.				
	1	(2)	3	4
I keep accurate lists of important things.				
	1	2	(3)	4
Work Organization				
I maintain an understandable file systems others can use when I am away from work.				
	(1)	2	3	4
I don't keep backlogs of papers and junk in my workspace.				
	(1)	2	3	4
I can find computer files easily.				
	1	(2)	3	4
My phone's calendar is easy to use and I use it consistently.				
	1	2	3	(4)
My workspace allows me to be productive.				
	(1)	2	3	4
When I need details on a previously scheduled meeting, I know exactly where to look to find information.				
	(1)	2	3	4
I do not let my work organization slip just because I am having a busy period at work.				
	1	2	3	(4)

I seldom ask for extensions or extra help in getting things done.			
1	2	3	(4)

I show up early for my work meetings and appointments.			
(1)	2	3	4

Home Organization

My house is my relaxing, happy place.			
1	2	3	(4)

My home is well organized.			
(1)	2	3	4

I seldom misplace things.			
(1)	2	3	4

I know where things are in my home.			
1	(2)	3	4

My drawers are well arranged and I find things easily.			
1	2	3	(4)

My closet is well arranged and I find things easily.			
1	2	(3)	4

My closet has a little extra space.			
1	2	(3)	4

I am able to let go of things I no longer need or enjoy.			
(1)	2	3	4

I am happy with the cleanliness of my home.			
(1)	2	3	⊗

I have company over as often as I hoped I would.			
(1)	2	3	⊗

I can find things when I need them.			
1	(2)	3	4

I return from shopping with everything I needed to buy.			
1	2	(3)	4

My DVD/Blu-ray collection is arranged systematically.			
1	(2)	3	4

I get out of bed easily and on time.			
1	2	(3)	4

I schedule time for myself to accomplish the things I want.			
1	2	(3)	4

I enjoy being in my home.			
	1	2	3	(4)

People trust me to show up when I make a commitment.			
	1	2	3	(4)

I know how long it takes to get ready each morning.			
	1	2	3	(4)

I never pay my bills late.			
	1	2	3	(4)

I re-hang my clothes when they are wearable again.			
	(1)	2	3	4

People tell me I am organized.			
	(1)	2	3	4

Add up your score by adding up the numerals you circled.

Obviously, the lower your score, the lower your level of organization! Read on to learn how you can increase your level of organization, starting today!

Chapter One: Why Are We So Disorganized?

In today's society there are a number of warring cultural forces. When we find ourselves bombarded by too many lifestyle choices, many of which are equally valid we have much greater difficulty making the decisions and priority choices we need to live more organized lives. For example, when faced with an excess of food—say, a buffet—humans eat to excess. This principle may also apply to areas beyond food.

Overabundance

One of the most compelling societal factors is our time of relative prosperity. We live in a world of abundance. As a culture we are faced with a bewildering array of choices. There are too many options and too much stuff out there to not lead to confusion.

While abundance is obvious when discussing material possessions, it is also a problem when considering non-material choices as well. It is Friday. That means a night of entertainment. Do you choose cable television, gaming, streaming? What about the play opening at the Little Theatre? Then there are the season tickets to the symphony you splurged for in a fit of cultural sophistication.

By the weekend you've had to make hundreds of choices about how to spend your time, energy, and money. If you have kids, Saturday will be another marathon of excess:

soccer, children's birthday parties, a swim meet, and a trip to the Discount Mega Mart for school supplies for a project due Monday. This pace doesn't even leave room for household activities that accumulate undone, for weeks, until the holiday season hits like a hurricane. Whew.

> Abundance is not bad in and of itself. But when over-abundance adds to your chaos instead of helping to address it, abundance can be considered a negative force in your life.

One last note on having an abundance of choices: research has shown that when there are a lot of choices, sometimes the decision maker ends up paralyzed. For example, the more options in a retirement plan, the lower the employee participation. Overabundance can lead to chaos when the abundance causes delays in decision-making.

Self-Indulgence

We've been told, "You deserve it," when faced with a choice—usually requiring the sacrifice of our money. Luxurious bed linens, entire chain stores of wonderfully scented bath oils and soaps, empowerment workshops. . . a bustling industry operates on the premise that you deserve good things, and that no one will give them to you unless you take care of yourself and give them to yourself.

Self-indulgence is not an intrinsically bad thing, but when it develops into habits that lead to disorganization, it becomes a burden to your life, not a soothing, relaxing entitlement.

Frugality

The frugality movement is a trend that operates in apparent opposition to the self-indulgence school of thought. And yet frugality, as described by many newsletters and books, is anything but simple.

One amusing example of frugality I once read about was saving those plastic six-pack rings that used to come on soft drinks. Did you know that if you save enough of those things, you could make your own volleyball net? While I believe recycling is admirable, I also want to be able to reside in my home. Unless I happen to be living in a four-acre warehouse, I am not sure my top priority will be to collect six-pack rings until I have enough to make a volleyball net.

If you are organized, many elements of the frugality movement will be extremely useful. Frugality can be a good thing—but if it causes you to become a pack rat, re-evaluate. Very few pack rats live serene lives.

Simplicity Movement

Legions of folks have 'opted out' and voluntarily downsized themselves into a way of life that they believe is easier, more pleasant and therefore more rewarding than the power career track. Some of the most fervent endorsements of this lifestyle come from the very people who occupied the power career track and were extremely successful at it.

The simplicity movement has its elements of frugality as well as elements of self-indulgence. But in many ways simplicity is not all that simple. It involves making many decisions and becoming skilled at making the decisions that result in a paring-down of excess in life.

To maintain a "simple" lifestyle, you must be ardent in the thinking and prioritizing skills that were used to downsize the life.

You may altruistically retire early to do important volunteer work in your life, only to find your Day Timer® packed with new obligations that drain just as much energy as your old schedule.

> The choice of a simple life is not a one-time decision, but rather a series of choices that must be upheld and reinforced by later choices, or the result will be a new lifestyle that is just as hectic and complex as the previous version—just in a different way.

Multi-Role Humans

This century yields opportunity for human beings as never before. Futurists predict the average worker will have seven careers during his or her work life. Not seven jobs, but seven careers. Now, add to these seven careers the non-work roles everyone assumes, such as spouse, parent, caregiver, volunteer, coach, housekeeper, chauffeur, and counselor. If you consider that for at least some of these career changes, new skills will require stints in higher education and/or vocational training, you'll have to add "life-long student" to the list of roles. This prospect implies a life of tremendous change and stress, peaking at various points around career switches, geographic moves and family emergencies.

Lifestyle upheaval is not only very stressful, but also very chaotic, even during the most well-organized transition. Given that at least some of these transitions will be involuntary, (i.e., caused by corporate downsizing, divorce, death, pandemic or natural disaster) the modern lifestyle—at least as envisioned by the early 21st century imagination—appears to be as challenging as the agrarian culture that suffered drought, floods and invasions in medieval Europe.

Minimalism, Tiny House, Van Life Trends

These three are the ones that pop immediately into mind when I think about current trends affecting personal organization. All three of these are very attractive to me, personally, although I am fairly sure they will be concepts I enjoy thinking about rather than adopting.

But I do want to point out that while each of these can be incredibly rewarding...they are not simple once-and-done lifestyles. Just as with simplicity, each of these require on-going, daily decisions to maintain the lifestyle. A tiny house, inhabited by someone not fully on board with the principles, will start to look like a jammed storage closet before too long!

Media Peer Pressure

Do you think peer pressure only comes from your peers? Think again. Marketers rely on the ease with which they can sway American opinions and desires. Social media is a huge transmitter of discontentment. It used to be that TV shows induced envy because we were so tempted to compare our average lives to the make-believe lives we peeked into. Now we get a first-hand look at everyone else's edited and air-brushed reality right from our smart phones.

This phenomenon of media peer pressure is actually worse today, because now we have a steady diet of home shows, cooking shows and gardening shows and DIY videos on every "self-improvement" topic on the planet. Now we don't just peek into impossible-to-really-live lives and homes, we get detailed "how to" instructions on creating the illusion for ourselves in our own lives. So now, rather than just a sneaking suspicion we had in decades past, we now have confirmation our lives are deficient.

The Result

These influences (and there are many more I could describe) pull us in many different directions at once, leaving us stressed out and tired. When we are under strain and tired, organization is one of the first things to fly out the window.

We're exhausted, so we leave a few things undone in the office as we leave for the day. We're tired when we get home, and so some of the chores we thought we might tackle get left undone. We go to bed late, because apathy left us watching the late news, even though we didn't care and are so stressed out by tomorrow's meeting that we can hardly cope with one more smiling newscaster telling us the latest crime statistic.

Still tired, we get up late the next morning, only to discover the undone chores included laundering the shirt we wanted to wear this morning. Leaving the house late, there's just no time to make breakfast. The drive-in line isn't that long, so we risk it and turn into the restaurant parking lot.

We arrive at work breathless, a few minutes late, with biscuit crumbs in the creases of our clothes, only to discover the work fairy didn't complete the items left undone last night. The meeting is in ten minutes, and it looks like this is the best part of what will only be a hectic, maddening day.

When you live like this, you are not in control—chaos is.

The Ten Principles

The thinking skills we will develop are based on basic principles of organization that will be first described, and then applied to some of the most common organizational challenges most people face. Much like taking a piece of cut crystal and turning it in your hands to refract shimmering light, these principles will be applied differently in different facets of everyday life. These facets, as in crystal, can be viewed multiple ways. For our purposes, we will look at "organizational thinking" as it applies to material objects, your social arena, your work and your home.

Self-discipline and Organization

As one popular self-help speaker has said, "Everyone has the same amount of self-control. It is 100%!"

Significant improvement in organizational skills is possible for everyone who is willing to change some behaviors, some thinking patterns and some actions. This book calls for change, and the most helpful types of personal change are almost always internally driven.

Discipline can mean rules and consequences for breaking those rules. But a better definition for our purposes might be this: Discipline is a practice that leads to you getting what you want out of life.

Think about it. In the areas where you need to have discipline to be successful, you are nearly always in pursuit of getting something better out of your life for yourself. Discipline in exercise? You'll live longer and healthier. Discipline in finances? You'll have the economic resources to do what you want with your money, instead of having your paycheck absorbed by paying for items you used up months ago.

Discipline in organization doesn't mean mindless adherence to strict, fun-robbing rules. Instead, it means expending the time and energy to conquer areas of chaos in your life, thereby freeing your energy to devote it to other, more rewarding, aspects of your life. When you are more organized, life is easier. When life is easier, you have more fun.

Let the fun begin!

Exercise 1

What is causing your to be disorganized?

Circle the societal trends that most impact you.

Overabundance

Self-indulgence

Frugality

Simplicity

Multiple Roles

Media Peer Pressure

Add others that occur to you:

Chapter Two: **What Does Success Look Like to You?**

Before we begin, there are some things you need to know about organization.

Clutter is the biggest enemy of organization. In our wealthy society, we simply suffer from too many options in too many instances. In this book I will talk about overabundance and how to cure it. Clutter goes beyond too many knick-knacks in the living room. It can include an overscheduled calendar, negative friendships that rob you of energy, and old commitments that no longer fit your life. With the help of this book, we will eliminate clutter in our houses and our lives.

An organized life is organized internally as well as externally. The tidiest closet in the world is of no use if its owner is in inner turmoil from disorganized thinking. The best laid out workspace is useless if you really hate your job. Clearer thinking is often associated with goal setting. Goal setting is linked to knowing what you want out of life. It is hoped that as you begin to organize your life, you'll spend more time thinking internally; specifically, about what you hope to get out of this book *and* your life.

Organization is ongoing. Just like housework, it has to be done regularly and at frequent intervals. The good news is that you can develop your own system so that being organized becomes a rewarding habit.

Organization is 95% making decisions. Chaos is the result of postponed decision-making. If you will hone your decision-making skills as you read this book, you will find yourself living a freer, more organized life.

Perfectionism is not your goal. We mustn't let the excellent become the enemy of the good. Stay focused on the big picture.

Invest wisely in the proper tools for your newly organized life. Quality file cabinets, the right household cleaners, and the appropriate tools are all essential to being organized. You wouldn't try to change a car tire without a jack, would you? On the other hand, many organization gizmos are just that—gizmos. Being able to store more stuff in a closet won't make that closet more organized, it'll just make it more full of stuff. So, you have to be careful choosing which tools are helpful and which are more of a hindrance.

Being organized allows you to set your priorities in order—in the order you want. You won't be ruled by your circumstances; instead, you'll rule them. By having determined your priorities you will be better able to focus on the things that matter to you.

You will probably find that as you become more organized, you can actually save money. No more buying another pack of AA batteries because you can't find the rest of the eight-pack you know you bought last month.

Is Getting My Life Organized Even Possible?

Applying the ten principles outlined in this workbook may look like a lot of work at first, but the results will be worth the effort. After a few weeks you'll find yourself applying them with very little thought.

> Just as reading a diet book will not make you thin, I am sorry to report that just reading this book will not help you be organized. You are going to have to *make* yourself organized.

Organization is not an overnight thing. Organizing your life will take some time. You'll be working to develop new thinking patterns and skills. Allowing yourself time to internalize the changes you are trying to make will increase the likelihood of permanent change.

You will have to be willing to do some homework each week. The more you do, the more expertise you will develop at being organized. If you don't put into practice what you are trying to learn, this book will not be very helpful. Just as reading a diet book will not make you thin, I am sorry to report that just reading this book will not help you be organized. You are going to have to *make* yourself organized.

*Organized living is not about rigid structure or inflexibility. It is about discovering what works in your life, and discarding or changing the rest. You are in control of this process.

*You may have to ask yourself some difficult questions and will probably have to change some of your habits.

*Acting on what you're learning is imperative.

*Stick with it! The results are well worth the effort!

Exercise 2

Create a Vision Board

Before we delve further into how to organize your life, let's spend some time thinking about what you hope to get out of this book.

A fun way to illustrate your thoughts is to create a visual image of what it is you are looking for. In the case of becoming more organized, it might be an uncluttered, serene house. Or a neat day planner. A spa-like bedroom, with beautifully arranged closet.

Take some time to figure out what you want your life to LOOK LIKE.

Then go online and search for images that depict those things.

You can search things like "neat desk" in Google Images and come up with plenty of ideas.

Find some that resonate with you, and copy and paste them into a new document. Resize the images as needed.

You don't have to really worry too much about copyright on this. You won't be publishing your vision board anywhere. It's just for you. As long as you use the images for personal use, you should be fine. If you decide to share your collection of images....that's another story! Let your vision board be private.

Here are some terms I searched for my vision board recently:

Master bathroom
Peaceful
Neat bookcase
Organized closet
Wood floors
Sleeping dog (represents peace and contentment to me)
Wardrobe
Small kitchen
Small garden
Porch swing
Cruise ships
Vacations
Walking (something I want to make more time for)
Gardening (a hobby I really enjoy)

Once you've gathered a few dozen images, arrange these in your document in a manner that is pleasing to you. Print this out in color, and put it in a place you will see frequently! I find that my bathroom is a great place for a vision board.

Chapter Three: **Self-Talk: time to rewrite your internal scripts**

We must learn to embrace our successes in order to help them happen. Begin by thinking of yourself as becoming more organized. Say to yourself, "I am becoming more organized every day," rather than criticize yourself with mental speech such as "You lost your keys again, you idiot," or "You're so disorganized it is a miracle you don't lose your head sometimes."

The more we say something aloud or even just think it, the more likely we are to continue to associate ourselves with that thought.

Numerous studies have proven the power of positive thinking. Negative thinking has the same power over us to fulfill its prophecy.

Exercise 3

Do you have any negative thoughts about personal organization that pop into your mind over and over?

Take some time to think about this, and jot down a few thoughts that may keep you derailed.

1.

2.

3.

What positive messages can you create to replace these thoughts? Write them down here.

1.

2.

3.

4.

5.

Transfer a few of these positive statements to small cards or other reminders and place them where you will see them during your day.

Chapter Four: Myths

Myths Surrounding Organization

Have you fallen prey to myths that make you feel hopeless? Some common myths about organization are listed below. You can probably add some of your own to this list.

If I just had a bigger house [or office], I'd be able to get organized.

The truth is, anyone can become more organized. Having more space to spread your disorganization around in usually results only in bigger areas of chaos.

For years, I dreamt about having a bigger desk so I could have double monitors and more room for pen cups and important folders and notebooks. Lo and behold, when I got, it just gave me more room to *place* things, rather than putting them away. Instead of on the shelf where they belonged, my binders were in a permanent stack in the corner. Instead of in the pen cup, my pens would be strown around my desk, making me strain myself to reach for them rather than keeping them tidy.

And worst of all? I found I can even misplace my screen cursor when using two screens! I probably look for the silly thing several times a day.

What happened? Why didn't the bigger desk help me?

Nature abhors a vacuum. And if you're messy with a 5'x 6' cubicle, odds are, you'll be messy in a 12'x12' cubicle, too.

More myths:

If I had more [shelves, closets, time] I'd be more organized.

Again, adding "more" to an organization nightmare without solving the underlying organizational problem only offers a short-term solution. Unless you increase your organization skills along with your space, the result will still be a larger problem spread over a bigger area.

Time isn't the answer, either, although sometimes we are certain it is. If your time management system isn't functioning well, you are not in control of your days and weeks. Adding more time without solving the underlying time management/organization problem will only result in your wasting greater quantities of time.

I'm just a disorganized person.

I am convinced there is no organization gene. Organization is a skill. Like any skill, it takes practice and work to master. But you can learn it and make it part of your daily life. You are probably relatively competent in many areas of your life. You may even be quite organized in many areas of your life. The trick will be learning how to strengthen your organization skills and then translate those skills from one area to another.

Organization is neat.

Some people focus a lot of energy on external appearances. But the truth is, an extremely organized and effective person may have a desk that looks like a rat's nest. There is no uniform "look" of organization. The key is determining the level of organization and orderliness that lets you accomplish that which you set out to do. The most important thing about any organization system is that it works for its creator. Thus, your picture of an effective kitchen may not be an uninterrupted expanse of empty counter surfaces, but rather a deliberate collection of the items you use most in the most logical places, even if it does mean you leave appliances out in full view all the time.

Exercise 4

What do you think *you need* to become more organized? More Space, time, energy, privacy?

Of these things, which really matter?

How can you get them?

Chapter Five: The Pareto Principle or the 80-20 Rule

The Pareto Principle is one of the most fundamental concepts in organization. To state it concisely, "Eighty percent of the value comes from twenty percent of the resources." Rather than trying to explain this principle, here are a few examples:

In your closet, 80% of your outfits are probably made up from about 20% of your favorite, most comfortable clothes.

You may have 40 icons on your computer desktop, but probably use only 4 or 5 of those programs every day.

In the kitchen, 80% of your meals come from 20% of the items you keep in the pantry. You probably have dozens of spices but use three or four most consistently.

In your office you use 20% of the space intensively, the rest only sporadically. Thus, the majority of your productivity in the office comes from a few square feet, probably the area in and around your desk and computer.

I've even heard the principle applied to committees—20 percent of the people do 80% of the work. I really can't disagree on that assessment.

The ratio may not be exactly 80-20, but you probably get the idea. In nearly every area of our lives there are some tools or resources that provide maximum benefit, and others that are rarely utilized. The smaller portion (supposedly 20%) you use the most is your critical area of concern.

The good news is that you don't have to get your life 100% organized. This book will try to help you focus on getting your critical 20% organized, so that the 80% productivity will flow smoothly. This goal applies to everything from where you keep your stapler on your desk to how to arrange your closet. By thinking about and applying this fundamental concept to most areas of your life, you will find yourself more organized and effective in the areas that matter most.

EXERCISE 5

Think of some examples of the Pareto Principle in your life:

1.

2.

3.

4.

5.

Chapter Six: The Ten Principles Explained (With Bonus Principle)

Just as with any field of knowledge, there are basic principles that can be applied to organization. Listed below are ten of the most important principles you can apply to an area of chaos in your life. In some situations, you may find yourself applying several principles at once. Other times, only one principle may apply. We'll go through these quickly now, with some illustrations to help you anchor them in your mind. Later we'll apply them to various aspects of everyday life.

Decide.

Most disorganization can be traced to postponed or unmade decisions. Sometimes we simply don't want to be bothered with making a decision. If you delay deciding something, you may spare yourself what may be a momentarily unpleasant task, but it will more than likely come back to haunt you later. For example, the question "Where should I put the W-2s?" calls for an immediate decision. By not deciding, they end up on the coffee table, the kitchen counter, the nightstand, and the dining room table. By April 13th, when you are looking for them, they are buried under four month's debris in five locations around your house.

Addressing decision-making with junk mail is very simple. A catalogue arrives in the mail. Decide: Am I looking for new [whatever is in the catalogue]? If the answer is no, toss the catalogue. If the answer is yes, browse the catalogue quickly and make another decision: Are the items in line with what I am looking for? If no, toss the catalogue. If yes, put it in your "catalogues to browse later" pile. And be realistic—not every catalogue that comes into your home needs to go into your browse stack! Decide quickly and you'll find your life a lot less overrun with catalogues.

The same postponed decisions can clog your work and social life, too. An invitation arrives in the mail, but you're not sure you want to commit. You stick the invitation on the refrigerator, where every time your eye falls on it, it adds stress to your life. You are reminded that you haven't decided to attend (or regret) an event that you are not really looking forward to. By deciding quickly and immediately phoning (or texting) your regrets to the hosts, you can toss the invitation and be free from ever thinking about it again.

At work most of us have to decide quickly about things. In many cases, other people are waiting on us. In some cases, though, others will wait, pausing their work while we ponder things endlessly. How to make quicker, better decisions at work? Realize that doing nothing is a decision.

If we are fearful of a bad decision, we may hesitate before making one. This delay gives us an illusion of safety. "I haven't botched up the ad campaign by choosing the wrong logo." But in truth, not choosing is a decision. By avoiding the possibility of choosing the wrong logo by postponing the decision, you may really botch the ad campaign by destroying its timeliness.

For some folks, work decisions come easily, but home decisions cause endless handwringing. Not making decisions at home turns into quick chaos. And perhaps because we feel safest at home, we're likely to tolerate more chaos. Unmade decisions abound. What to cook for dinner? Can't decide, therefore nothing gets defrosted and you wind up eating out. Again. It seems minor, but the cost of this minor chaos adds up in terms of time away from home, energy drain from wearing your "public manners," credit card bills and expanding waistlines.

How to decide? Sit down once a week and create a menu. Go ahead and make quick decisions—if it is not fit for a five-star restaurant, no big deal—and you can always select another menu next week. But making the decision in advance takes the pressure off you—you don't have to re-decide every evening.

EXERCISE 6

Your thoughts: Can you think of a time or two when not making a decision quickly caused things in your life to get messy? Explain.

If in doubt, throw it out.

This concept might be my favorite organization principle. I know it is the one that produces the greatest peace in my life. While it applies to most aspects of your life, it is especially valuable when applied to paper. If you are looking at a blanket memo that conveys information you already know, just pitch the memo in the trash. Ditto with unworn clothing, weird metallic pieces in your kitchen drawer and nearly expired taco shells you probably won't eat. The best way to apply this principle is to get in the habit of asking yourself, **"What is the worst possible thing that could happen to me if I throw this out and later need it again?"** In the vast majority of cases, the answer is nothing. You might have to go ask for a copy of that memo from the secretary who sent it. Maybe you have to make a trip to the hardware store for a metal doohickey to replace the one you tossed. Usually. the worst-case scenario is not only very unlikely to happen, even if it does, we're talking minor inconvenience, not the end of the world. Get in the habit of purging all non-essential items immediately. You'll be amazed at the sense freedom you gain.

This principle applies to other aspects of your life as well. Do you have a friendship that, while it was once joyful, has become a burden? You find yourself screening his or her phone calls and feeling exhausted when you don't. Maybe it is time to go your separate ways. Are you still a member of the track club, even though your running shoes haven't been used in years? This might offer another opportunity to "throw" something out of your life.

At work we think mostly of papers—but when you're evaluating things to throw out, don't forget emails. Do you have somewhere along the line of 4,867 messages in your in-box? If so, you need to do some weeding. If you've been keeping emails for future reference, make it a point to sort the important ones into appropriate files. Then, those that are left dangling in your inbox can be automatically deleted after a set period of time. Some email programs do this purging automatically.

From the pantry to the garage, you'll likely find hundreds of "doubtful" items in your home. How do you tell? It is easy. You know the keepers—those things that you know you want to keep no matter the cost or hassle of storage or maintenance. If you have to play a scene in your mind attempting to visualize a case where you might use an item—you are experiencing doubt, and it's a good indication that it is time to let it go.

BONUS PRINCIPLE: If in doubt, don't buy it.

The best way to address excess anything is not to add it to your life to begin with. When you are considering a purchase, ask yourself, "Where will I use this? Where will I store it when I am not using it? Is it likely to end up in a garage sale? How often will I use it in the next three years?"

When you have to wrap your mind around a purchase and imagine a future use, you probably don't need the item. For example, you see an almost new chainsaw at a great price at a garage sale.

"Cool. A chainsaw! I could use one of these. Let's see—one day that tree in front of the house might grow up to be big enough to need its limbs trimmed. Then there's the chance it might blow down in a storm. Yeah. A chainsaw will be good to have on hand." If this is the internal conversation you have in your head—a potential use that is years down the road—you don't need a chainsaw.

Don't buy things for grandkids you don't have yet. Don't buy party supplies for parties you have not planned yet. Don't buy things because they are a good price, smell good, look good, are well-built or for any other enticing reason.

Only buy an item when you have a real need for it and have a place to store it when you are not using it.

Exercise 7

Your thoughts: Can you describe a few occasions where you hung onto materials items that really were better let go? What about non-material items, like memberships, relationships, etc.?

Use it or lose it.

How many items are you warehousing in your office and home? Are there items that you haven't used recently and are unlikely to ever use again? A good rule of thumb with most items: If you haven't used it in a year, odds are you can live without it. Yes, there are exceptions. You don't have to send all the camping gear to Goodwill just because you didn't use it last summer. But if you know that you hate camping, and only did it to show the kids how to rough it, maybe it is time to purge the gear.

Try the "Have I used it in a year?" question on the contents of your home. If you've got pots, pans, clothes, books, furniture—whatever—cluttering up your life, put it to the use test. If you're not using it, prepare to "lose" it. (Our other principles will help with this effort.)

True confession: I actually gave away or sold most of our camping gear several years ago. I even had a tent I had never even set up! But, as my husband and I evaluated our travel styles, his need for a CPAP machine (which can be difficult to manage when there is not power at a campsite), and other preferences, we just decided that we wouldn't use the gear enough to justify the space in our attic that we gave over to storing it.

Fast forward to 2021. We were invited along on a camping and rafting trip with some friends. We have no tent. We have only one sleeping bag. Having been through a few hurricanes and the loss of power that follows, we did have a camp stove.

Our solution: we decided to try out van camping, and camped in the back of our Honda Odyssey. We put a porch swing cushion in the back seat foot well to level out the floor of the van, removed the middle seats, stored the back row seats, laid down some yoga mats and we were set to camp. It was summer, so we just took some sheets.

I am so glad we did not reinvest in a tent. And, when the others were dealing with packing up a damp tent and damp sleeping bags, we just rolled up our yoga mats and were ready to go.

Exercise 8

Your thoughts: Make a list of ten things you are keeping for no logical reason at all:

1.

2.

3.

4.

5.

6.

7.

8.

9.

10.

What are some ideas about yourself that may have to change if you get rid of some things? For example, I once got rid of all my size 2 and 0 clothes after finally admitting to myself I wasn't likely to ever get in those sizes any time soon. (And I was surprised by the relief I felt.)

A more poignant example is a mother I knew of who kept a bread baking machine that she never used. She said, "If I get rid of it, I'll have to admit to myself that I am not the kind of mother I planned to be—a mom who makes her kids fresh bread!" Wow!

I had a similar situation when I donated all my books about "owner-built homes" to a local library. All during my youth I had planned to become a hippie, live off the grid (this was before I even knew what a grid was!), with a solar powered, underground/dome/tree house with composting toilet. I planned to grow all my own food, organically, of course. After I married my dreams changed, and now I live in a 100+ year old house in an historic neighborhood. Despite how much I love my house, husband and life, giving up those books meant I was giving up on my dreams. It was hard to let go of them.

Exercise 9

What things are you hanging onto that represent meaningful things to you, but which no longer fit your life?

Point of Use is Critical.

Do you know many people who keep their office phone in their bottom desk drawer? Probably not. Most people prefer to keep the phone handy. Some even subconsciously place the phone on the side of their "good ear." This is a great example of the point of use principle. Items used every day must be kept in places where they are accessible and easy to use.

Unfortunately, after the telephone, people sometimes don't do so well at keeping things handy. Are there items you find yourself looking for again and again? If the answer is yes, you know you need to relocate those items to more functional places, which may mean taking an inventory of the items you keep in your prime space and making some deletions. For example, if you frequently find yourself reaching for a phone directory at work, it may mean a closer, more convenient place would be helpful. No room, you say? I suspect that if you purged your desk drawers of files on dead and/or completed projects, you'd have the space for the directory.

Again, point of use is critical, and if you're using valuable real estate at work to store dead files, you're not employing this principle.

Recall the Pareto Principle. If you get 80% of your productivity from 20% of the items you keep near you at work, you really want to make sure you have the best 20% at hand.

Here's how to apply this principle. If you have items you use regularly, figure out how many movements they are away for use. For example, you keep your pens in your top drawer. Left hand opens, right hand reaches, and you are ready to write. That's two reaches away. Not bad. If you had to swivel your chair, scoot back, open a drawer, grab a pen, swivel your chair back and scoot back to your desk, that's not good. This principle sounds like common sense, and it is. But it is also very easy to let things wind up in awkward places accidentally. Plan to relocate things while you make your life more organized.

What about non-thing things? For instance, a gym membership at a gym that was close to your last job—but 45 minutes from your new one? That's too far away to be really useful, unless you happen to have an extra 90 minutes in your day for the extra commute.

Is your church far from home? It may be the best fit for your family. But if distance is really getting in the way of your participation in church life, maybe something needs to be changed. The best organization in the world isn't useful if you don't participate in its programs.

You can also apply this principle to your computer files. Do you have to use your "find" command once or more each week? You've got a point of use problem. Are there files you use over and over for an intense period of time? If so, you have probably learned to put them on your desktop— or some other convenient place. But do you make it a point to relocate them to better archival positions once you are not using them as often? Don't give up valuable real estate to dead files—whether it is desk space or virtual space.

Point of use is also critical for a smoothly operating home. I'll share some real-life examples from my home. First, I have ugly office-style trashcans in almost every room. Why? Because I want to be able to throw things away now. I know that if I stack a bunch of things neatly to be discarded later, it is very likely these things will end up "inter-stacked" with things I want to keep and I'll have to re-sort the whole stack at some future point. I also keep scissors in a drawer in almost every room.

I keep Windex ™ in every bathroom, the kitchen, and the laundry room. I use it a lot and know I am more likely to keep things tidy if I can just grab the Windex ™ and go. I also keep white paper towels nearby. Other things I keep handy are spices and cooking utensils. I want them to be no more than 2 reaches away from the task. (I really do not like to cook and if I make it any more of a chore than it is, I enjoy it even less.)

Exercise 10

Your thoughts: Name three things that are kept in inconvenient places in your home and three things that are kept in inconvenient places in your work setting?

What is the reason these things are kept in inconvenient places? Does that make sense for you? Is there are a better place

Determine a place for everything.

We just talked about point of use being critical. Fine. But this is where the rubber meets the road. You must *decide* where things go. This is critical to that 20% of stuff that you use frequently—be it clothes or spices. But what do you do with the other 80% of stuff that makes up your universe? You must figure out where they go now, tomorrow and forever more.

This problem area is where postponed decisions have made your life miserable. When you haven't already decided, once and for all, exactly where you are going to keep items, you end up looking for them repeatedly. Decide on a proper location for each item.

An example I see all the time: women digging through their purses for their car keys. (Sorry to stereotype, but it is true. And it can be a safety issue if your distraction makes you vulnerable to predators.) Anything you go hunting for again and again needs the application of this principle. Going back to our first principle, DECIDE where you will keep your car keys. Decide once and for all that no matter which purse or briefcase you use, your keys will always be put in the same place—say the outermost pocket. There. Put them back each time until a habit is formed and now you know where your keys are every time. Even if you switch to a backpack for a day hike, using the "place for everything" principle, you can put the keys in your pre-determined place, the outermost pocket, and know where they are.

Where do you store your extra office supplies? Or your vacuum cleaner? The vinegar? Your VISA card? If your answers to these questions vary with the phase of the moon, plan to decide now where you are going to keep items. As you finish using them, stop and consider, "Where is the most logical place to keep this item?" Bear in mind the point of use principle. You don't want to keep the kitty litter stored 30 feet from the cat box. One way to determine where to put something is to ask yourself, "Where would I look for this item first?" As you determine proper locations for things, steadfastly return them to their proper places until a habit is established.

This idea even works for appointments if you determine the place to track them is your calendar. If you've set good limits and you have a "place" for all your events, a glance at your calendar (you do have one, right?) will tell you if you can accept a new obligation.

Exercise 11

Your thoughts: Name five items that you routinely misplace?

Where do you keep them?

Does this change often?

Could you come up with a final answer for where these items will be kept in the future?

Handle it once.

Do you find yourself moving things around and around your workspace and home? Does it seem that you sort and shuffle stacks of papers repeatedly? If this is the case, you are probably handling things too many times. Try to develop the habit of handling things just one time. For example, when you finish using a power tool, put it away. Avoid setting it on the workbench "for now." Go ahead and put it where it belongs. Otherwise, it will likely wind up buried beneath 12 other objects that get added to the workbench "for now."

The deadly "for now" causes chaos in many lives. Develop the habit of sorting the mail once. [Decide.] Move the clean laundry once—i.e., fold it when it comes out of the dryer rather than toss it on the dining room table, the bed or the couch, where after several days it is so wrinkled you have to wash it all over. "For now," is often just a code word for "more work."

This concept is especially critical when it comes to papers. When a paper enters your life, learn to deal with it immediately. It may seem like a time saver to set a sheet aside to deal with later, but more often than not, you'll find yourself with an 'In Basket' that remains full, causing you to shuffle through it several times a week to find things.

What about meetings? Are you discussing the same meeting topics over and over? If every committee meeting seems to be re-hashing the same old issues, you may be "handling" an issue too many times without really addressing it. Could it be that a postponed decision is bogging things down? If "old business" remains the predominant focus of every meeting, you'll need to find ways to speed up decision-making. This acceleration could involve anything from inviting people of greater authority, who can address the problem, or deciding the problem has no ready solution and moving on.

Exercise 12

Your thoughts: Do you have items that you needlessly shuffle through over and over?

Name several of them.

1.

2.

3.

Brainstorm for ideas on how you can eliminate the shuffle.

1.

2.

3.

Set limits.

To control clutter, chaos and excess, set a maximum number and stick to it. Do you collect penguins? Decide that you will never keep more than 25 at a time. When holidays result in your collection growing, weed out the less desirable penguins until you are at your target number. You can also loudly announce at Thanksgiving that you no longer collect penguins, thank you. (I used this on my accidental duck collection. It worked.)

Do you find yourself keeping nice boxes for gift-wrapping? Set a limit, say 4 boxes, and stick to it. When a new box comes into your life, compare it to the others and keep the best four. The same methodology can be applied to those nifty string-handled gift bags and shopping bags.

What about social events? You might decide for peace of mind to never schedule more than two social events during any single weekend. By setting the limit, you don't have to re-decide every time your calendar starts to fill up. After accepting the first two invitations, you simply say, "I'm so sorry, but I'm all booked up the weekend of the 8th. Thank you for inviting me. I'm sorry I'll miss all the fun." This technique also works on volunteer activities and church committee assignments.

I know of one family who, in the interest of getting to see their own children on a semi-regular basis, decided to limit extracurricular activities to one per semester. Were these "deprived" children able to recover from this arbitrary limitation on their lives? Yes. In fact, both went to a private college on full scholarship.

The freedom here is that no one is told they cannot save rubber bands, pretty string-handled bags, or mayonnaise jars. They can keep them forever if they wish. But they can only keep a set number and excess gets recycled. Chaos is controlled, and the collector is happy.

Exercise 13

Your thoughts: How do you feel about limits? Are they freeing? Or do you find them negative and restrictive.

How can you use limits in your life to gain more free time? How can you use limits in your life to help you avoid overload?   Write down some possibilities.

Recycle, reuse, release.

As you get better and better with your decision-making skills, you are going to find yourself with a problem: what to do with that which you do not want or need. Processing this "stuff" will require responsible action on your part.

Recycling is very popular now. But there are more ways to recycle than to put things in to color-coded bins. As you consider your home and workspaces, are there objects that no longer have a productive use for you? If you no longer enjoy something, or it no longer adds utility to your life, consider getting rid of it.

There are many ways to "recycle" things. A good habit to develop is to give things away freely. Let's consider the purple cow creamer Aunt Martha gave you. You never liked it, but your neighbor collects cows. Pass it on. You'll enjoy having it out of our life, and your neighbor will be tickled at the kitschy addition to her collection.

Giving at work can mean returning to the supply cabinet office supplies that clog your desk drawers. Or passing along the never-used transcription equipment to someone else.

Of course, there is always Goodwill and The Salvation Army and even those handy color-coded bins. The idea is to begin thinking about what you can delete from your life painlessly. It is probably more than you realize.

We all enjoy some traditions. But there are times when a tradition outlives its usefulness. Has a tradition become a meaningless chore for you? If so, here is a chance to creatively "recycle" the tradition into something that is more meaningful to the people involved.

One family I know had several members involved in retail management—which meant from the day after Thanksgiving to early January a family gathering was out of the question. So, they moved Christmas to the summer. Why not? It is not illegal to put up a Christmas tree in July. (You might want to hold off on the exterior decorations, depending on your neighborhood covenants.)

I got a delightful family newsletter in September this year. It was such a pleasure to read and it didn't get tossed—unread—into a stack of Christmas cards. I thought it was a great idea. To "recycle" the newsletter from the holiday season to a time when life is less hectic made the newsletter more enjoyable to both the writer and the reader.

Another recycling method is to use objects for purposes other than those for which they were intended. If you have a number of lovely crystal vases that remain unseen and unappreciated in a closet, why not use one as a pencil holder? Your old golf bag with the built-in cart could be a handy yard tool caddy. The point is, don't be a warehouse; either use an item, or give it to a good home that will.

The ultimate point behind this principle is to hold onto things with a loose grip. The harder we cling to something, the more work it becomes. One of my class members shared a great idea that illustrates a loose grip: throwing a rock at her car.

You know how when you get a new car you tend to be meticulous about taking care of it? Maybe you haven't done it, but I have—sometimes going to extremes of parking in the outermost parking spaces to avoid those inevitable nicks and bumps the paint will suffer.

My student would throw a rock at her new car, thereby eliminating the agony of trying to avoid the first ding. That's a loose grip, and a much more peaceful position than the anxiety-filled "pre-ding" mindset.

Exercise 14

Your thoughts: Can you think of times when "holding on too tightly" to material things has caused you problems?

Think about how you can develop a mindset that allows you to let things go easily. What are some things you could let go of now with few to no consequences? Why are you hanging on to these things?

Do one more thing.

As you leave an area, consider what "one more thing" you could do to make re-entry into that area easier when you return. As you leave the kitchen, what five-second action could make things better when you return? Wiping the jelly off the counter before it turns to hard goo? Rinsing the sink? Putting the cereal away? Or maybe even getting the cereal out for breakfast the next morning.

At your workplace, about five minutes before you leave, pause to do one more thing that will make your arrival at work easier the next day. Could you jot down a list of top priorities? What about pulling out the file for the project you will begin in the morning?

Think in terms of small, concrete steps you can take that will make re-entry easier. If you make it a habit to do one more thing each time you move from one activity to another, you will find you've already begun your task when you return to the office, or kitchen, or whatever. This method will make re-entry easier, focus you more readily on the next task at hand, and reduce the "dreads." Really, who wants to face a kitchen with hardened grape jelly cemented to the counter?

Exercise 15

Your thoughts: Thinking about your place of work, what is a concrete step you can take each time you leave that would make your re-entry to that area more pleasant? How about as you leave your dwelling? What about as you exit your car?

Try to think of ten instances of "leaving" an area where you can add on a 3o to 90 second task that would help you when you come back to that space.

Don't collect junk.

Become extremely picky about what elements of your life you keep. Life is too short to clutter it with junk. Junk can be odd mementos given to you by well-meaning friends, outdated (or uncomfortable) furniture, or other objects that no longer bring you pleasure. Junk can even be bad relationships that only depress you and deplete your energy.

Start now by eliminating the things in your life you just don't like. Never liked houseplants, but people gave you several when you were sick? Give them away or put them out of their misery.

There is more junk at work than the odds and ends in your desk drawer. What about useless assignments? Extra committee appointments? Meetings to plan meetings? At one organization I was affiliated with there was once a Committee on Committees! Doesn't that sound like fun?

Unless you are the CEO, you can't really jettison work assignments at your own will, but you can take up the discussion, tactfully, with your boss if too many non-essential tasks are impeding your work on priority projects.

Try to view your home and office with a critical eye, as if you had never stepped foot in the door before. You may enjoy offbeat décor, and that's fine. But is there anything downright tacky present? If so, relieve yourself of the burden.

And then there's "Junque." Do you have antique furniture that no one can sit in because it is too fragile? It is junque. Pristine white carpet in a room no one's allowed to walk in? Junque. Just because it is expensive, valuable or pretty doesn't ensure worth. If it adds to chaos in your life—or just headache and hassle—it is really junk.

Does the Bovine Club membership you keep no longer bring you fun and fellowship? Maybe it is time to resign. Sometimes purging your life of a time worn object or commitment can be scary. Purging something will leave a vacuum, and most people usually strenuously avoid vacuums. But consider this: a vacuum can be a place of peace and serenity. And just because a vacuum may exist in your living room when you get rid of the ugly orange chair, you don't have to rush right out and get a new one. Live with the vacuum a while, and then decide what you want (if anything) for that space in your life. It may well be that the peace you feel from ridding yourself of burdensome objects may more than compensate for the loss of a chair.

Then there is another kind of junk altogether. It is the emotional-strings-attached junk that insinuates itself into your life. One day in my organization class, a woman had tears in her eyes as she described a painful pressure point in her home. Her mother-in-law had given her a large, fragile, blown glass sculpture. It was kept in the living room. Not only was it not to the woman's tastes—its delicacy meant her three small boys were essentially banned from that room.

She felt this ugly (but expensive) sculpture was holding a good portion of her home hostage. My advice? Break it! That may sound harsh, but after talking to this woman for several minutes, there seemed to be no other solution. So, I suggested she let her kids play with Frisbees in the room in hopes an errant toss would take out the sculpture. (I might have simply dropped in on a tile floor myself.)

Breaking this item may sound extreme—but the mother-in-law wasn't about to let it be put into storage. They couldn't sell it at a garage sale. And the mother-in-law wasn't exactly ancient, either, so they could not bear the thought of it simply trying to outlive her.

To liberate herself from the emotional control her mother-in-law exerted, breakage seemed a worthwhile choice. After all, what could the mother-in-law do upon hearing the sculpture was broken (to smithereens)? Kill a grandson? Not likely. Buy a new one? She probably would not trust them with a new sculpture after the careless breakage. Would she get mad? Probably. But we had established that she was already going to get mad with every other possible removal scenario. At least this scenario had the mother-in-law getting mad and the offending sculpture gone. You'd hate to put the thing in storage, have a family feud over it, and then be forced to put the horrid thing back on display.

This example leads to my next point about junk. Be very careful from whom you accept "gifts." If Aunt Lucinda is going to go berserk if you re-cover her divan, don't accept it unless you love its upholstery.

Consider the giver's track record. Does this person ever "checkup" on the status or location of gifts? Does she ask you where things she gave you are? Has she ever asked any family member to return a gift? If so—don't accept things from this person unless you really want it, love it, and intend to keep it (pristine) for the rest of the giver's natural life.

How to say no? Try telling the giver that you simply don't think you'd be a good steward of such a "valuable" item. If that doesn't work, try the truth—you don't want it. She may get mad. Given her track record of strings-attached giving, she was likely to wind up mad at some point or other anyway.

Exercise 16

Your thoughts: Isn't there some junk or junque in your life? Name ten examples.

1.

2.

3.

4..

5.

6.

7.

8.

9.

10.

Do you have toxic gift-givers in your life?

If so, what are your plans for dealing with them?

Exercise 18

What kind of decision maker are you?

Take this quiz

I cannot make decisions easily. Yes or No

I often regret my decisions.   Yes or No

I agonize over decisions, sometimes for so long that I don't ever actually make the decision, it just becomes irrelevant.   Yes or No

I am a slow decision maker.   Yes or No

I am just not good at snap decisions.   Yes or No

I need a lot of information to make a decision.   Yes or No

I seldom go with my gut a lot when it comes to decision making—that seems irresponsible.   Yes or No

I over analyze things.   Yes or No

Analysis paralysis could describe me.   Yes or No

After I make a decision I become more anxious than before I make up my mind.   Yes or No

I am afraid my decisions will turn out to be bad decisions.   Yes or No

How many of these statements describe you?

Many? Just one or two?

Exercise 19

Practice strengthening your decision-making muscles by deliberately becoming more bold and ruthless in your decision-making in areas of your life where it is okay to practice. For example, tackle removing outdated foods stored in your fridge. Ask yourself, "Am I willing to eat this?" and if the answer is anything but an unqualified and enthusiastic "Yes!" toss the food in question.

Do a self-check afterwards. How did that feel? Is it okay to decide to let expired food or old leftovers go?

Try the same thing with your daily clump of junk mail. Go through it quickly and ruthlessly.

Do a self-check. Are you comfortable with getting rid of catalogues before you've perused them?

Exercise 20

Find areas in your life where you can practice making quick decisions. Jot down some of the quick decisions you've made.

Go back to your notes a few days later. Any issues with your quick decisions?

Did some of your quick decisions lead to feelings of relief? A reduction of stress?

Spend some time thinking about decisions in your life. Write down three areas where

postponed decisions are creating pressure points in your life.

1.

2.

3.

What can you do to address each of the above? What is stopping you from making decisions that you need to make?

Chapter Seven: The Foundation of Organization, Clutter Removal

Okay, you've read the ten principles. Now it is time to put them to use. Following the simple instructions below and using the ten principles, you are ready to conquer some chaos. Read through the entire exercise, schedule your assignment (see Appendix A for complete instructions) and start getting organized.

Go ahead and schedule a time several days out. Write it down in your calendar. This interval gives you mental preparation time. Arrange for curious family members or co-workers to be out of view and earshot. Serious de-cluttering doesn't lend itself to an audience.

Gather some boxes.

Four to seven medium cardboard boxes. Boxes usually stand up, and so they are best. Plastic garbage bags may be substituted for some of the boxes.

Label the boxes as follows:

1. Garbage

2. Give away (Salvation Army, church jumble sale, etc.)

3. Relocate (not mine, not here!)

4. Doubt

5. Alter or repair

6. Borrowed and need to be returned

Exercise 21

Step One:

Select a well-defined area of chaos to start on—something concrete with clear boundaries, such as the closet or the car, or maybe just a tabletop or desktop. Don't attempt to conquer the entire house in your first session or you'll wind up discouraged at the magnitude of the task.

You may be excited to start organizing your life, and want to use your energy on a big project. Don't do that just yet. We will get there, I promise. For now, take something small with defined boundaries: the top of your dresser, or the top shelf of your closet. Don't tackle the entire closet at this point. We want to start with some successes, but also have a meaningful conversation about the decluttering process.

The area I am going to declutter is:

_____

Bonus: Take a picture of the area you are about to tackle. Before and after photos can be very rewarding!

Now, set up your sorting boxes. And don't forget the 'privacy' you'll need. You won't get far on this if you have a screaming audience wailing over every item you try to purge.

Keeping the ten principles in mind, *quickly go through the area*, placing items in the appropriate box. For things that belong in the area you are de-cluttering and organizing, set them aside neatly, so you can get them put back in their proper places when you are finished.

It is best to go quickly. ***Trust your first judgment and keep moving***. Studiously apply the ten principles. If your "Doubt" box fills up first, you are not deciding—you are postponing decisions. Dump out your "Doubt" box and start over!

Step Two:

After everything is sorted, go through the "Doubt" box with a hard heart and sort it into the other boxes. Sort every item into the other boxes. You have to resolve your doubts now. Remember, "If in doubt, throw it out."

Step Three:

Next, deal with the **Alter or Repair box**. Are you really going to have the work done? If the truthful answer is no, get rid of these items, too. If you really will invest the time and money on the repair, make a plan for it to happen. If it involves a trip to the repair shop or alteration shop, jot these on your calendar or to do list. Or delegate them to another family member. Put the items in your vehicle so you can take them where they need to go (repair shop, alterations place, etc.).

If you really plan to fix the broken vacuum cleaner, put it in the car, maybe even the front seat. Keep it visible (and irritating), so you will be forced to do something about it. Do not stash the seven "Repair" items in a closet and pretend they do not exist. We are trying to reduce chaos, not add to it.

Step Four:

After everything is sorted, take the boxes to the appropriate place. Do not stack the boxes in the garage or carport. Do not cram them in a closet. Make it a point to deal with them.

Throw away the garbage box today. Take it out to the curb, even if trash collection isn't for three more days. If your family seems overly curious or concerned about the contents of the garbage box, take it to a dumpster, put it in front of a neighbor's house—anything to keep your family from picking through the box and digging out treasures.

Deliver the "Relocate" box to the proper rooms. If they are open, take the charity box to Goodwill, Salvation Army, etc., or put it in your car for delivery the next day. As for the borrowed items, put them in your vehicle as well. If you have time, start returning them today. If you do not have time, make an appointment in your calendar to return the borrowed items this week.

Step Five:

Now, put the remainders back in their proper places, using the ten principles. Make sure your most-used items occupy the 20% hot zone. For a linen closet, this means the most used items at easy reach level. The extra pillows for the seldom-used guest bedroom can be higher up. You get the idea.

Excercise 22

Once you have decluttered an area—do a self-check. How do you feel?

Chapter Eight: Rationalizations

Before you read this chapter, do at least de-cluttering exercise mentioned in chapter seven. It is critically important to complete at least one "de-cluttering." That experience will make the content of this chapter more meaningful. If you haven't practiced decluttering, stop now and go do it. Clean out your wallet or purse if you have to. But declutter something!

Finished? Okay, read on!

Most of us consider ourselves to be rational beings, making decisions based upon well-thought-out ideas and plans. At times, however, we rationalize our way into a clutter-keeping trap. The biggest problem I hear about from my students is the pain of getting rid of things. They add things to their throw away box, then they sneak an item or two back out. For every two that go in, one comes back out.

Finally, some decide it is hopeless and come to class and try to convince me they absolutely had to save the items they kept. Below are some of the things they tell me.

Do any of the following rationalizations sound familiar to you?

"This might really come in handy someday."

The number one protest I hear in my organization class is, "But I might need it someday!" Yes, you might. But then again, you might not. If you think about the unlimited possibilities of life, virtually every object you ever touch might be theoretically needed "someday." Do you really plan to keep everything you ever touch? Of course not.

So, ask yourself: on that imaginary day when you actually need this item again, what will happen if you don't have it? Will it be life or death? (Keep the nitroglycerin tablets!) Or will it be only a mild inconvenience? Or will it not matter at all? That pack of seven birthday candles, for example. Yes, keep them if you have a child under seven. But if all your kids are grown and it is unlikely that you'll ever use just seven birthday candles, go ahead and toss them. If you keep them and tell yourself you'll buy more to go with the seven when you need twelve, you'll discover that the new ones don't match the ugly old ones anyway. You'll just toss them back in the drawer where they will be in your way every time you reach for the kitchen scissors. They'll aggravate you until your estate is settled and your executor puts them where they really belong—in the trash!

"This was made back in the days when quality and craftsmanship mattered."

That's probably right. But are you actually using that object's fine quality to enhance your life, or is it just taking up space? You can admire fine workmanship without owning it. (Besides, if it is an appliance, it probably won't have polarized plugs, and you'll worry about its safety and never use it anyway for fear its wonderful quality will burn your house down.)

"It reminds me of [something significant]" and other emotional clutter traps.

I hate to tell you this, but Granny's not in that lamp! Yes, things do remind you of people you love or places you've enjoyed. But they are only symbols of the people or places they remind you of. Thus, if you discard a pair of miniature wooden clogs, you won't be destroying The Netherlands. And your memories that are triggered by the clogs are held in your heart and head—not in the wooden clogs. So, if the wooden clogs no longer bring you daily joy, but instead add to the clutter you must maintain, dust and keep arranged—get rid of them!

If the trinket brings you joy each time your eyes fall upon it, by all means keep it. But if the memories are stale and no longer rewarding, feel free to liberate yourself from the physical symbol. I'd guess that if you are considering letting it go, you are ready to let it go.

> *A note on gifts: No matter how hurt people are when they find out you've moved (or even discarded) their gift, they really cannot expect to control you for the rest of your life by forcing you to display an object you do not enjoy. You are not betraying that person by getting rid of an object. Your love remains undiminished. Communicate that thought. Keep things out of joy, not guilt.*

If you have gift donors who really feel that you are honor-bound to do as they wish with a gift, you have several choices. You can do as you wish, risking alienation from a person who wants to control you (maybe not a bad thing). You can do as you wish and they may never give you anything again (again, maybe not a bad thing). You can refuse to accept gifts with strings attached. Or you can accept the gift gracefully, with full knowledge of the strings attached. If you do accept the gift, you should not harbor ill feelings towards the donor; after all, accepting the gift was your choice.

Overcoming Rationalizations

No one likes an argument, least of all with oneself! But here are a few ideas on combating rationalizations that result in your keeping everything.

One way to "argue" these rationalizations with yourself is to try and put a cost on maintaining the questioned item. If there is only a 1/100th percent chance you will ever need the item again in the next decade, is it worth 3,650 days of living with it, moving it around, dusting it, air-conditioning it, and keeping track of it? Probably not.

Another question to ask is what percentage of your life will you devote to storing excess clutter? If ten percent of your home is filled with clutter, is it worth ten percent of your mortgage payment to continue to warehouse it? How many hours must you work for the dollar amount you are investing in needless storage? If that amount seems insignificant, get a finance person to calculate its future value. That'll be eye opening when you consider that amount invested in your retirement rather than the mini warehouse you'll eventually need. (If you don't already have one now.)

A third question to ask yourself is this: If I persist in keeping this stuff, what will happen to it when I die? Odds are very strong that your heirs will send most of it to Goodwill or the garbage dump without so much as a loving glance. Half-finished projects, old catalogues, 8 track tapes. . . all of this "stuff" will wind up either in a landfill or on the shelves of a thrift store.

The final word.

Now or later, your clutter will be dealt with.

You can sort it now. Choosing how and when to disperse or dispose of it.

You can wait until you are aged and infirm and try to deal with it when you break up housekeeping.

Or you can leave the problem to others and let your heirs plunder through it. But don't ever doubt that one day everything will be dealt with. You cannot take it with you.

Exercise 24

How hard was it to discard or giveaway stuff that had no future use for you?

Did you find yourself trying to start an internal argument to keep some things?

Write down some of the reasons you decided to keep things.

After reading chapter four, what are the rationalizations that plague you the most?

Copy down from the book (or write your own) statements that help you overcome your "must keep" rationalizations.

Chapter Nine: Moving Forward

Now that we have looked at the Ten Principles, evaluated and (hopefully) improved our decision-making muscles, attempted a test run of decluttering, and finally, assessed our rationalizations that hinder us in letting go of things, it's time to get started on organizing our lives!

Yay!

As you continue to read the book, go through this workbook. Plan to devote time to yourself at least weekly.

If you really want meaningful change, you'll have to devote time to practice. This practice is called homework, and ideally you should set aside two to four hours for it every week as you work to get your life organized.

Plan to return to this workbook weekly and continue to work at areas in your life that are really an annoyance.

Let's start by figuring out which areas require your attention.

GOAL SETTING FOR PERSONAL ORGANIZATION

Goal-Setting Exercises

An unrecorded goal is merely a wish. A documented goal is an action plan. If you will take some time to work through the exercises on the next pages, you will be surprised at the result. There is something powerful about taking the time to consider and write out goals.

When you couple your written goals with action steps—as indicated in the exercises that follow, your goals are even more powerful.

This exercise will lead you through an evaluation and help you set priorities for the areas which cause you the greatest angst. Start with the areas that bother you the most, in small, concrete pieces.

Exercise 25

Goal Development

Evaluate your situation. Spend 30 minutes going around your home (or office — whichever is your primary focus) with a note pad. Open every cupboard, closet, drawer, etc. Take notes of what bugs you. Which room is the worst? As a result of your inspection answer the following question:

The chaotic or disorganized areas that I need to work on most are: (list in any order)

Now let's think about them.

To determine how big the issue is, ask yourself this question in each area: "What are the negative consequences I face if I do not improve in this area?" The areas with the greatest negative consequences should be circled. Don't forget to calculate non-tangible consequences—such as daily aggravation.

Of the above areas, circle five that are the biggest issues for you.

Now, again thinking in terms of the consequences or personal costs involved, rate the circled areas from One (Most Important) to Five (Of Lesser Importance).

Exercise 26

Looking at the previous page where you prioritized your organizational projects, rewrite them below, in order of priority. Add in as many details as you can.

1.

2.

3.

4.

5.

Your list might look like this:

1. Living room. Hang picture over mantle, clear up magazines and papers. Find a place for the extra coffee table (Goodwill?) Rearrange accessories to a better configuration (eliminate some?)

2. Office. Figure out a filing system. File those papers on top of the filing cabinet. Set up a folder or some system to pay bills regularly.

3. Storage room. Clear out all junk and haul it away.

4. Kitchen. Organize the drawers and figure out where the stuff should go. Do SOMETHING (anything) with the pantry.

5. Master Closet. Try to set it up so I can find something to wear without trying on six outfits every morning.

Exercise 27

Once you have identified your top five priorities it is time to create measurable goals and plan for action steps that will get you where you want to go!

For each of the areas listed above, use the following pages to develop a GOAL for improvement and ACTION Plan to address the area. Start by transferring the item on each line above to its corresponding goal sheet. (Next pages.) Reword the item into a goal.

Exercise 28

Goal Number One

My goal is:

My deadline for accomplishment is:

Here are the steps I can take to meet this goal:

Time Frame	Action or Step

A reward I can give myself for accomplishing this goal is:

Goal Number Two

My goal is:

My deadline for accomplishment is:

Here are the steps I can take to meet this goal:

Time Frame	Action or Step

A reward I can give myself for accomplishing this goal is:

Goal Number Three

My goal is:

My deadline for accomplishment is:

Here are the steps I can take to meet this goal:

Time Frame	Action or Step

A reward I can give myself for accomplishing this goal is:

Goal Number Four

My goal is:

My deadline for accomplishment is:

Time Frame   Action or Step

A reward I can give myself for accomplishing this goal is:

Goal Number Five

My goal is:

My deadline for accomplishment is:

Here are the steps I can take to meet this goal:

Time Frame	Action or Step

A reward I can give myself for accomplishing this goal is:

Chapter Ten: Realizing Your Goals

Now that you have written five organizational goals and created action steps (plans) to achieve them, let's go a step farther.

Exercise 29

Get out your calendar (or open it up digitally) and, starting with the first goal, start blocking out time to accomplish each step you have outlined. Describe the step fully in your calendar so that you can start the step without back tracking to your goal sheet.

A likely first step will be to take action using the declutter process described in chapter seven, eliminate all excess items in each of your priority areas and rearrange the remaining items in a manner that is pleasing to you. Use the ten principles to guide you. Reread them as often as necessary!

Exercise 30

Some Contemplation Questions

As you completed the described activities, think about your reactions to the clutter elimination process. Was it difficult? Easy? Did you find yourself becoming motivated to do more, or less?

What was hardest?

Did you set priorities for areas to be addressed?

In looking at your list of what bugs you the most, was there a pattern from room to room or area to area? What kind of thing disturbs you the most? (For me, it's floors. If I can keep floors spotless I am much happier wherever I am.)

Thinking about your de-cluttering actions,

How did it go?

Was it hard to let go of some things?

What emotions haunted you? Fear? Sadness?

Was it a relief to let go of some things?

What worked best for you: small blocks or large blocks of time?

Chapter Eleven: Calendars

Your calendar needs will likely be different at different points in your life. If a calendar is not working, go and find another style. Time is too precious to squander on a bad calendar. In my case and at this point in my life, I have found it better for me to have a single calendar where I log in personal and work commitments. I still keep a giant 12-month calendar on the wall in my office, where I write in all my special projects (and planned vacations) because I need to see my year visually to grasp how my time is used. When I see a month filled with four or five colors of notes, I know without even reading them that I need to steer clear of more commitment for that month.

Once you have settled on a calendar style, here are some pointers.

It should be big enough to write in all necessary details. A birthday party on Saturday? You'll need time and place—and maybe even the honoree's name. Make it a point to put as much information in the calendar as you need. Don't just say "party" and then scramble around for the invitation Saturday morning.

Examples of details you should make a point to note: date, day and time of meeting, length of meeting, topic, and what items you should take with you. Emailed invitations are great for this, because they will link automatically to the calendar notation.

Your calendar should foster communication across various aspects of your life. By this, I mean you should be able to record all sorts of details from various parts of your life, such as church, home and work on it. A calendar you carry with you does this easily. So does a web-based calendar, since you have access to it from almost any location. If you have a calendar, but fail to note things on it, you really just have a paperweight.

When you use a calendar well, you should also use it for yourself. I mean, remember to schedule into your life periods of time to get your own stuff done. If you need two hours twice a week to write, schedule them in. Use ink! Make your status "unavailable" and use that time to achieve your goals.

Exercise 31

Make a plan to maximize your Calendar's function.

Your thoughts: How do you need to improve your calendar-keeping?

What are three action steps I can take, starting today, to better utilize my calendar or scheduler?

1.

2.

3.

How will I know I have improved in this area?

Now, take a moment to locate a date and time about 14 days from now, and schedule in a self-check to review your improvements in your calendar keeping.

My appointment with myself is on
_____.

Once this date has arrived, what further action do you need to take? Are you complying with action steps outlined above? Why or why not?

1.

2.

3.

Chapter 12: Dealing with Papers

In dealing with paper problems, it is best to take a multi-faceted approach. Eliminate paper at its source, attack the incoming stream, and then conquer the backlog.

Here are our organization principles with just paper in mind.

Decide.
Like most disorganization, paper problems are really postponed decisions. Learning to make quick decisions the first time you encounter a piece of paper is critical.

Decide what to keep and what to toss. Then actually toss the things that deserve it. Remember my Point of Use Principle and the trashcan in every room?

If in doubt, throw it out.
By asking, "What's the worst thing that will happen to me if I toss this paper?" you will find that many of the annoying items in your life can be quickly dispatched.

Use it or lose it.
Are you hanging onto files you've never consulted? It has been reported that 80% of what gets filed in the typical office is never looked at again.

Do you have instruction manuals for appliances you no longer own?

Point of use is critical.
Papers you can't find when you need them are utterly useless. You might as well not even have them. Filing is

essential follow-through for paper organization. A stack on top of a file cabinet is not filed. Set aside time to put papers away on a regular basis.

Determine a place for everything.
Just file it! For the papers you decide to keep, it is imperative that they have a home. Permanent residence in your "In Basket" does not count.

Handle it once.
Do you find yourself circulating paper around and around your desk, home or car? If so, you have the perfect opportunity to learn to handle papers as little as possible. If you have to handle papers more than once--for example, keeping bills to pay on payday--at the very least you must learn to put them in a place reserved for unpaid bills and nothing else.

Sound overwhelming? Remember, once you learn to make quick decisions and cull ruthlessly, you'll have fewer papers to handle.

Set limits.
To reduce your paper load, set limits on how many papers you'll hang onto. Perhaps you will save only the best of the best of your six-year-old's artistic creations.

Likewise, how many of your own creations are you hanging onto

Recycle, reuse, release.
Let's be honest, most recycling in this area will have more to do with getting the paper into the recycling bin than with passing papers along to more appropriate parties.

However, in workplaces, papers often arrive at your door that belong to others or can be delegated. Learn to pass this paper on immediately.

Do one more thing.
This principle leads you to complete one more, small task before you leave an area. Regarding paperwork, what additional small step could you take to complete your handling of a paper item? Could you go ahead and browse the catalogue and then put it in the trash? Could you file the memo you just read? Or toss it? Add information from papers to the place it belongs.

A lot more energy goes into remembering not to throw away a piece of paper than it takes to go ahead and deal with the contents of the paper.

Don't collect junk.
Is it really necessary? Will it be outdated in a few weeks? Don't let the habit of saving every little scrap of paper turn your file system into an archive of irrelevant garbage.

The Paper Questions
To help clarify your decision-making, ask these questions when it comes to paper.

What is the worst thing that could happen to me if I throw this away?
If the answer is nothing--throw it away.

Where should I keep this piece of paper?
Decide where the proper place for the item is as soon as possible and put it there

Once I put this piece of paper in its proper place, how will I know where to find it again?

The best way to decide where to put things is to simply decide, go ahead and create the file folder, box or whatever, and then consistently put like items there until it is a habit. How do you decide? It is easy. Simply ask yourself, where would I look first if I wanted to locate this paper again?

How long should I keep it?

When you set up a filing for something, you're almost guaranteeing it'll still be in its manila folder when you retire or downsize. Before you archive things, make sure you really need them. If you decide to keep it, consider putting down a "throw away after" date on the file.

Where will I deal with my paper?

At home and in the office, determine a single place to deal with your incoming paper. Pick just one place.

Potential paper problems

On the surface, this approach all sounds so simple, because it really is. But beneath simple principles are underlying human tendencies. Do any of the following sound vaguely familiar?

Wishy-washy decisions:

Not deciding is a postponed decision! You know postponed decisions result in chaos.

Control Issues:

Decide who will be responsible, and put the papers in the appropriate place

Exercise 32
Handling Papers

Before you begin to address a paper backlog, stem the incoming tide!

Action Checklist:

_____Sign up for e-statements whenever possible.

_____Cancel any subscriptions you no longer enjoy.

_____Keep a trash can where you sort in-coming papers.

_____Determine what monthly statements are also available online.

____ _____

____ _____

Your thoughts: Make a plan to attack a backlog (the big purge)

What is the first backlog you plan to address:

When will you conduct this paper purge and sort activity?

Is the area concrete or specific? Is it contained enough to be do-able in one sitting?

What is the most important question for you in deciding what to keep and file versus what to toss or shred?

Chapter 13: Setting Up a Tickle File for Work and Home

Paula Royalty, a leading organization expert, describes pending items as the number one paper problem in America. A pending item is an item you need again too soon to set up a file, but not soon enough to finish with it right now.

The problem with these pending items is that they sit around and by the time you need them you may have no idea where the items are, or you may have to sort through a three-inch stack to find them.

To avoid pending paper problems, you can set up a very simple system to track them until the papers are required. These systems are often called tickle files. All you'll need is an accordion pleat file.

Here's how it works.

Office supply stores sell accordion pleat files with one section for each day of the month. These files would make a suitable tickle file, as you can simply drop the item into the slot for its date. Others are available that have alphabetical slots, or slots for the months of the year. Think about your time frames and pick a type that will work for you.

For every piece of paper, you'll have to determine an action date. For many papers, the date is set, such as appointments and meetings. With these papers, you jot down all the pertinent information on your calendar or to-do list and then file the papers in your tickle file under the date.

For example, if you have a proposal to be discussed at next month's Product Review Meeting, simply note the time, date and place of the meeting on your calendar and file the relevant documents under the tab for the date in your tickle file. Make a notation on your calendar that refers to the file. If you need to peruse the proposal before the meeting, jot an additional note on your calendar a day before the meeting that refers to the proposal. Now the proposal is off your desk, but reminders have been fully documented.

It's okay to intermingle items for March 15 and April 15 in the same tab. You know where they are, and you will only have to look at the tab for "15" when the time comes.

For on-going items, the key is to select a date at which you will take the next step in the process. Jot this newly created artificial deadline on your calendar, and file the item in your tickle file. Again, the paper is off your desk, but retrievable. With your calendar notations, even if someone asks you about it before the action date, a quick look at your calendar will tell you where to look.

And you can create tickle files for individuals in your family—say, one for each kid. If you come across a recipe daughter #1 will like, drop it into her tickle file. Next time you are together, just pull out everything behind her tab.

Exercise 33

Your thoughts: The best tickle time frame differs by individual. Which is best for you, twelve calendar months, or 31 days of the month?

Do you need a tickle file for people as well, say co-workers or family members?

Decide on a time when you can set up your tickle file.

I will set at my work tickle fine on: _____

I will set up a home tickle file on:_____

Now, make a notation on your calendar for both of these appointments and also—about three or four days prior—an appointment to shop for any needed supplies.

Chapter Fourteen: Your Mission Statement

Exercise 34

Spend some time thinking about your top three to five priorities at work.

My top priorities (at the moment) are:

1.

2.

3.

4.

5.

Do any of these have deadlines? If so, note them.

Now, thinking of the next 90 day period and your top priorities, craft a mission statement of what you must have accomplished on these priorities in the next 90 days.

Do this same exercise for your home. What are three to five things you plan to have or do in your home in the next 90 days?

1.

2.

3.

4.

5.

Note any deadlines.

Now, craft a statement of intent for these items.

Self-Check:

Do these items appear in your primary goals that you developed beginning on page 73 of this workbook? If not, why?

Make any adjustments needed.

Type up these mission statements and post them in a local you will see frequently throughout the day.

Chapter Fifteen: Organization at work

First, end distractions.

The biggest task in better organization for an office setting is to eliminate all unnecessary distractions. Distractions can be people or things — including papers, unnecessary tasks, technology and other irritants.

End digital distractions! By this I mean news sites, social media sites, and your favorite (time-wasting) websites. If you find yourself wasting time on digital platforms that do not help you meet your professional objectives find ways to block these sites.

Put your cell phone away. If you use it for work, keep its ringer on, but put it out of sight.

Turn off all notifications that you can turn off. Train yourself to check for notifications at set times each day. Don't respond to each one individually.

Use your company's intra-communication platform to set "Busy" status and "Do Not Disturb" status.

Use your email's auto response to let people know you are working on a deadline and will be in touch after you meet the deadline

Exercise 35

Your thoughts: What are your top three time-wasters or distractions at work?

1.

2.

3.

What can you do about each one?

1.

2.

3.

Second, keep track of things.

Having (and using) a daily planner (digital or paper) is essential to good organization. If you do not have one yet, make it a point to get one and use it. You cannot trust your mind to hold all the details you need to remember. If you don't have a calendar yet, stop and get one—because you can't de-clutter without a way to track the essential facts on many of the papers you eliminate—and many of these facts will belong on a calendar.

Exercise 36

**Your thoughts: Describe your calendar system?
Does is synch with other elements of your life,
like home?**

There are many free options online that will allow you to check your calendar from anywhere you have internet access. Start with your organizations and find out if remote access is a thing. (I am sure it will be, because what organization doesn't want you available 24/7?)

Exercise 37

List three ways you can improve the use of your calendar.

1.

2.

3.

Third, schedule yourself an office declutter day!

If you have a large (or dysfunctional) workplace seek privacy. When you decide to de-clutter your office, try to do it on a weekend. It is better to do this work alone, and when you can take the stuff to the dumpster discreetly. You don't need your co-workers commenting on your progress.

Exercise 38

**My appointment to declutter my office and purge papers
is:_____.**

Clutter is your biggest enemy. When our offices (or primary workspaces—whatever their form) are cluttered, inefficiency is the natural result. When you have to move four or five other projects to clear a working space for the current project, you not only waste time, but you also increase the likelihood that you will be distracted from your primary goal and/or lose something in the shuffling process.

The basic cure is to first get rid of the excess stuff in your office or workspace. Extraneous papers, varied forms of professional reading, even "award" paperweights all have one thing in common: they require your time and attention.

I recommend that you first employ the basic de-cluttering technique to your primary workspace. For the purposes of this chapter, I will assume it is an office, but it could be a lab, a workshop, or whatever. The same principles apply.

De-clutter by employing the clutter removal technique described in chapter seven. Set up boxes for Garbage, Give Away, Doubt, Borrowed (if needed) and Keep. (Hopefully you won't have much in the repair category—but if you are warehousing broken equipment, create that category, too.)

Exercise 39

Action step: Do you have your boxes/trash bags ready and labeled? (If not, round something suitable up!)

Then, using the ten principles, work your way through your workspace. I'd start with something easy with clear borders—like your desktop, rather than something overwhelming, like the back warehouse. Examine each item with the principles in mind and ask, "What's the worst that could happen if I got rid of this?"

Don't obsess about potentially making mistakes. Just work your way through quickly.

Exercise 40

My plan for office decluttering is as follows:

First priority:

Second Priority:

Third Priority:

Additional: If I have time I will also:

Once you have decluttered, you need to reduce the intake

Before acquiring anything, ask yourself how it will help you in accomplishing your mission. Your office is not intended to be a warehouse! Be very critical in evaluating and retaining new items in your workspace.

If you are parking something on a bookcase, credenza or desktop only because you cannot think of another place to put it, re-think your decision. Determine the best place for the item, and immediately take action to ensure it gets to its better location.

Reduce "Other Clutter"

While most of us think of clutter as "stuff," it can also be tasks. Be slower to say, "Yes," not because you are unhelpful, but because you "want to focus your energy on your top priorities." Use this line when you want to say, "No." Try to avoid life clutter of annoying obligations that only decrease your energy and focus.

Other clutter can also be office gossip, discussions of last night's game, or any number of other non-work-related distractions. You can be selective about the amount of time you invest in the more trivial of office activities.

Beware the New Filing Cabinet Syndrome

If your filing system is effective and you always easily find information you need, then you might discover you have a real need for a new filing cabinet. Before adding one in this instance, I'd consider a serious purge of older files. By purging (use a shredder, if necessary) you may delay the purchase.

If, on the other hand, your system is a disaster with your filing cabinet crammed full and you can hardly ever find anything without a major struggle—**definitely do not** buy a new filing cabinet!

Instead, work on addressing your filing (or lack thereof) issues first, purging useless paper and filing things appropriately. Adding a new filing cabinet to a chaotic filing system is just a fertile greenhouse for more chaos. It may hide the chaos, but it's still there.

Exercise 41

Your thoughts: Do you purge your files regularly?

Do you have plans for more filing space? Why or why not?

Prevent "Sticky Note-itis": Make your reminders significant

Is your workspace covered with 3M sticky notes? You probably use these notes as reminders. Have you ever noted something on one of these lifesavers, but still missed the appointment or deadline? Here's why. After you have more than one or two posted, your brain learns to ignore them. If you leave little reminders around as permanent décor, they become a part of the routine static your brain has learned to filter out.

Exercise 42:

Have you ever missed an important piece of information, even though it was "in plain sight?"

Take a moment now and remove any temporary reminders and put them in a better place.

For permanent reminders (phone extension directory, etc.) make it a permanent installation in a manner it won't fall off and go missing.

Employ the point of use principle

Remember the Pareto Principle—the 80-20 Rule? Take dead files off your desk or out of the front of your filing cabinet. You might consider grouping supplies and materials on a project basis, so when you turn your attention to a different task, all the needed supplies are in a single place

Use Your Energy Well

I had a boss who wrote scholarly books. Despite a grueling workload and responsibilities in four states, he still managed to write hefty tomes on subjects way over my head. He used his energy well. I noticed he seldom scheduled morning meetings, or if he did they were at 7:30 a.m. I suspect that's because he used the morning hours for his writing. That's a really smart thing to so.

Exercise 43

Do you know if you're a morning person or an afternoon person?

If your brain works better on one schedule than another, try to complete your most important assignments when you're at your mental and physical best. If, for example, you know you're almost useless until 10 a.m., try to spend your morning hours doing tasks that are less challenging. Maybe this is a good time to schedule your correspondence activities, answer email and return phone calls. If you can get away with it, maybe you could schedule those boring meetings during this time.

Exercise 44

How can you rearrange your schedule to better use your "peak performance" times?

Stay on Task

Using your "Mission Statement," focus on your specified project. Resist the urge to be distracted. Keep your To-Do list handy, and continue to add to it as your mind brings items to the surface that will need your attention later.

As you come across material objects that need attention, or files that belong to a co-worker--put all of these in a single place to deal with at once.

By always keeping a list handy (I keep an Excel spreadsheet just for this) you can literally do a brain dump every time a list of niggling (or critical) items comes up. Once you've written it down, you can let it go, knowing you will get back to it. You know you won't forget because you wrote it on a list.

If at all possible and appropriate, delegate.

Delegation can be tricky for some people, because they like to hang onto authority. Learn to give away responsibility when it is appropriate. To be fair, when you delegate a task, you should also grant the authority to get it done. Nothing is more frustrating for a subordinate than to have a responsibility without authority. For example, we've all run into a professional, pleasant customer service representative who could empathize with our problem, but who could not solve it. That situation aggravates everyone involved.

Before delegating a task, ask yourself a variation of the question we've used repeatedly, "What's the worst thing that will happen if this is never done?" If the answer is "nothing," consider letting the task go altogether. Employees are quick to see busy work; if it is busy work, that means there is real work going un-addressed.

Delegate to other's strengths. If you know your subordinate's strong points, you can delegate tasks that reinforce these strengths. If you know Mary is a terrible public speaker, but Jim enjoys it, send Jim to make the presentation. Yes, as a supervisor you must "grow" and "stretch" your subordinates, but choose the occasions to do so where the payoff is greatest and the risk least.

Delegate with specifics. Assign a task with a built-in accountability structure. Every assignment should have a due date as well as clearly articulated expectations. Unclear assignments result in unclear products. While you outline due dates and expected outcomes, it is best to allow the person a choice in exactly how to meet the deadline and objective. If you feel you must provide step-by-step instructions on how to do something, ask yourself, "Is this a control issue for me, or do I have an inexperienced subordinate who needs guidance?" If you spend as much energy delegating in minute detail as you would in completing the task you have either a control problem or a subordinate problem.

Delegate with real deadlines. When you tell someone you need something "as soon as possible" you really aren't saying much at all. Instead, give a specific time. "I need this by 1 o'clock so that I can review it before I meet with Jim." ASAP might mean, "when you get around to it," or "when your other priorities are accomplished."

Exercise 45

Your thoughts: Do you have a few tasks that can be delegated?

Make a list of these. Start arranging for these tasks to be given to others better suited for them.

Then, being honest, are there things you are doing that benefit no-one? Probably not, but do a self-check, just in case.

Get to work on time

It may be a no-brainer, but one of the biggest things you can do to be more organized at work is to get there on time and well rested.

Exercise 46

Do you have "getting to work on time" issues?

Or, if you work from home, do you have problems with meeting deadlines? If so, why?

Spend some time thinking about where the issue lies and make plans to address it. Rome wasn't built in a day, so how can you begin to address this? What are a few steps you can put in place to help with this?

1.

2.

3.

What else can you do?

Create a promise to yourself to address this issue in the next 90 days:

Chapter Sixteen: Technology

Don't let technology manage you!

We often elevate technology to the level of a taskmaster instead of a helper.

How many of you are slaves to email? Is it difficult to not check your email every fifteen minutes or so? How many of us interrupt almost any activity, including sleep, when a smartphone pings? It is easy to let technology take over.

Exercise 47

Your thoughts: Thinking about technology, from annoying text message alerts to the temptation to binge-stream a show until the wee hours of the morning, evaluate technology and its impact on your life.

Are you a cell-phone-aholic, scarcely able to go an hour without a phone fix?

Do you get sidetracked into websites, going down digital rabbit holes?

Is gaming an issue for you?

Does social media absorb your time?

Does is make you happy, angry, sad?

Do you binge watch streaming apps to the detriment of your sleep?

Do you ever feel you are missing out on real life and real relationships because of the time you invest in devices?

The problem with much of the technology at our disposal is that it is absolutely habit forming! We literally get addicted to "likes" or addicted to the digital reward of cat videos.

Exercise 48

Do you have digital habits you want to break? If so, list them.

Now, create an action statement for each one. What is a better habit you can substitute? Write down one or two options for each statement.

Here are some concrete ways to deal with common technology-based problems. Before considering these, remember that the ten principles apply here, too. A simple decision to not react to every incoming email message can be a big relief. You can realize that subscriptions to multiple e-newsletters is only marginally useful and have your name removed from some of the lists.

Email

If your computer gives an audible chime every time an email message comes in, you are acutely aware of every new message. How much time do you spend transitioning from your current activity to the email platform? If it is only a few minutes each time, over the course of the day that could eventually add up to an hour or more. Try to address your email load only once or twice each day. Dealing with several email messages at once will help you to ration your time. When you see 16 messages needing a response, you'll be less likely to spend too much time on a single reply.

Before dealing with incoming email, be sure to delete junk or spam the moment you get it. Don't let it build up until your inbox is useless.

Ask yourself if a reply email message is really the best response. Maybe something old fashioned—such as the telephone, would be more helpful. This choice is especially true in cases where you are negotiating things. Rather than jockey back and forth six times in setting up a meeting, call the person and ask them to open their calendar and look at theirs while you look at yours.

There's also the option of saving yourself a little bit of time by using automated responses. If your computer sees that you normally respond to emails with a "Thank you, will do!" it can have that option ready for you to fill in your email, click send, and be on your way to other pressing tasks. And for routine correspondence, there is no need for eloquence.

Oh—and don't send "You're welcome" replies to emails that simply say, "Thank you." Especially when it involves "Reply alls!" Ugh!

Virtually all email programs have "folders" where you can archive items by sender or topic. If you find yourself hanging onto email messages (and you are absolutely certain this is essential and not just an electronic form of clutter) be sure to file them, rather than leaving them in one big pile in your electronic in-basket.

Exercise 49

Your thoughts: What are some ways you can deal with email better?

Telephone Management

Do you manage your phone, or does it manage you? Do you pick up every phone call all the time, or do you schedule blocks of time where you let your phone roll over to voice mail, thus allowing yourself a period of concentrated work?

When blocks of time are needed, use your phone as a tool. It will capture messages from folks who call you during your period of concentrated work.

On your outgoing voice mail greeting, consider recording commonly requested information. Your fax number or email address, for example, or hours of operation, if appropriate. Also, instruct callers to leave information that is helpful. Do you want a brief message, or a detailed recitation of the caller's issue? Say so.

When calling someone else, a few pre-emptive moves will make your time a better investment. For starters, jot down a list of issues that you hope to address in the call. This approach will keep you on task and also serve as a guide of what to mention if you wind up leaving a message.

When you do reach voice mail, be sure to clearly identify yourself. Don't just say, "This is Barney." He may not know your last name or what department you work for. Again, indicate how many items you are addressing, so the person you are calling doesn't delete your message after the first request. Leave your phone number every time you call.

Exercise 50

Action Step: Re-record your voicemail greeting if needed.

Cell Phone Organization

There's no doubt that smartphones have changed our lives in many ways. With a few taps of our fingers, we can pull up the weather forecast, restaurants in our area, photos our friends posted just *seconds* ago from vacation in Cancun, news reports—the list goes on and on.

Since our phones are such a convenient and versatile storage device, they are often overlooked and neglected when it comes to decluttering and organization.

Enormous phone storage is great. But how frustrating is it to really want to locate a picture of something important and you can't find it because you're scrolling through fifty-something pictures of your cat lying in the sun?

To bring back a point I made earlier: abundance can be a hindrance on productivity.

Your phone may be another area of your life that needs some serious decluttering, and that's okay! It's easy to just swipe away notifications from the screen that aren't useful—but what if there weren't notifications there to start with? What if you got rid of some of those apps you haven't opened in months, yet you still get seasonal sale notifications from? You probably wouldn't miss them.

Think about it: when is the last time you picked up your phone and didn't have a list of notifications or alerts to look at on the screen. Start turning needless notifications off.

The biggest hurdle with cellphone organization is time. If you're like me and have neglected the task, it's going to take some serious dedication. But the best part is it doesn't have to be done in a day.

Start small and work your way up.

If in doubt throw it out. Use it or lose it.

No, not your smart phone! I'm talking about all those apps you downloaded for a specific purpose that's long gone, or a test run that they flunked. If you have several unused icons on your home screens, it's time to free up space by letting them go.

Delete the unnecessary.

This means uninstalling apps that you haven't touched in a while or won't touch in the future.

You might find yourself holding onto unnecessary mementos within your phone. This includes notes, messages, or photos. Emails stack up as well. Delete the ones that you don't need to clear up your inbox a little. Make this your waiting room game: sort and clear your phone when waiting.

Exercise 51

Action step: When can you spend small amounts of time doing this? While watching TV?

Figure out some concrete times and enter them in your calendar to remind yourself.

Organize your apps.

Before I created my own system on my home screen, one thing I found vexing was dealing with so many apps. I hated having to swipe through multiple screens to figure out where the app I was looking for was located.

When I was younger, my approach to this was minimalistic: I tried to cram everything I needed on one singular page of my phone. This meant if I downloaded something new that pushed me over to Page 2, something had to be deleted. As you can probably tell, this was not the best way to go about organizing my phone, but I had a lot less going on back then, so it worked for that small period in my life.

Here are a few more ways to organize your apps:

- By function (productivity, finance, entertainment)
- By usage
- Alphabetical order
- One screen (though I don't recommend it!)

Exercise 52

Action step: Next time you have a few minutes to spare, instead of spending time on social media, spend that time uninstalling apps you don't use.

I have an iPhone, and I find it very useful that Apple gives you a static bar of icons to keep at the bottom of your home screen. You cans elect these and easily move them around to whatever you find is most convenient. Currently, I keep my phone, Microsoft Teams, Safari browser, and Outlook email in that section.

Reevaluate what push notifications you receive.

Personally, there's just something about notifications that really grates on my nerves. Especially if I'm already in a sour mood from something else; seeing all those red numbers beside my apps makes my anxiety shoot through the roof some days.

Likewise, the same can happen for pop-up or drop-down notifications. It takes more energy (and time!) than I have somedays to sit there and swipe all of them all my screen.

This is why I like to take a moment after installing an app to figure out what kind of notifications I want to receive. Is an update about every sale necessary? Nope, so I turn it off. It keeps me from having something else filling up my screen—and also from egging me on to make purchases I haven't planned.

Exercise 53

Action step: This is a great waiting room activity: go to your device's settings and look for the notifications section. You can scroll down and review each app and set its notifications to settings that relieve you from alert fatigue.

Use Cloud storage.

Now, I understand sometimes we might not want to just get rid of everything, even if we have a crazy number of duplicate pictures of our pets or kids. I find it easier to back everything up in a separate storage on the cloud and then delete the pictures or files from my phone.

Here are some cloud storage devices to choose from:

- Dropbox
- Amazon Cloud Drive
- OneDrive
- Google Cloud
- ICloud

Exercise 54

Your thoughts: Do you have any surplus files or photos that would be better stored elsewhere?

Smart Devices and Productivity

With the decluttering of our phones done, we can move onto making our devices a true tool of productivity for our lives. When I first started this process, my phone was more of a distraction than a helpful tool. I would get on it and scroll and scroll to keep myself from focusing on the tasks at hand.

More recently, it has become a lot of things for me: a timer, a reminder, and a work device I can use when I'm not in my office, etc. A lot of this process involved finding the right apps or techniques to use my phone for, rather than just a social media device.

Track your usage.

IPhones have a built-in system that reports on Sunday morning your usage for the week before. If your phone produces such reports, turn them on and critically examine the results.

Exercise 55

Your thoughts: Is your phone time well spent?

Conveniently, cell phones can also give you an option to schedule downtime in your day. This allows you to choose which apps are available to you at certain times. Say, if you really need to work on a project from 2:00 p.m. to 5:00

p.m., you can make it so your social media apps are unavailable to you between those times! (Hey—you can do this for your kids' phones, too!)

There are also options to set time limits on apps, communication limits within your contacts, and which apps are always allowed. It's a really great tool for those of us who impulsively turn to our phones at the earliest sign of a lull in our days. (And there are desktops apps that do the same thing.)

Use your calendar

It really helps to sync your calendars, especially if you're a person who likes to write things down on a physical calendar. I try to make time at the beginning of a busy week to make sure all of my important dates, meetings, or deadlines are put into my digital calendars as well. These serve as great reminders throughout the week because they tend to pop up on the screen when I power on my computer, or as notifications on my phone.

I use a crazy mix of Microsoft and Apple products, and I can still have everything sync across all the devices. And I am not the world's best geek by any means.

Additionally, calendars can be used for events outside of your work schedule, so make sure you keep those updated as well. Digital calendars are great for keeping yourself up to date on birthdays, doctor's appointments, bills, and payday.

If you don't like the current calendar system your phone has, here are few helpful apps:

- 24me
- Google Calendar
- Microsoft Outlook Calendar
- Pod
- Vantage Calendar
- SolCalendar
- Today Calendar

Use your camera to help you remember.

Sometimes the camera can be a great tool to help us remember things that may slipped our minds!

Take pictures of items you want to buy, so you'll have the exact item in front of you when you go to the store.

I keep a picture of the back of my car because I'm the worst when it comes to remembering what my license plate number is (even after all these years.) And how about a picture of where you've parked? My phone actually records this information. But when I am at a huge and unfamiliar venue, it never hurts to snap a pic of the nearest signage.

I've snapped photos of my car and health insurance cards, my AAA card, and a lot more.

Take pictures of your pantry and fridge before you go grocery shopping, so you don't rebuy products you thought you ran out of. I also like to use the screenshot feature on my phone when I'm online and want to check something out later because I don't have time to look at it now.

Oh! And capture images of wine labels when you find one you like. Probably the best use of a camera phone there is.

Keep digital lists handy.

I mentioned earlier the concept of having an Excel file open on a tab in my browser, so that when random things pop into my head at random moments of the day, I can just click over to the spreadsheet and make an entry.

I do the same things with a notepad on my smart phone.

I have entered things like my husband's clothes sizes, name brand of dog food my dog prefers and so on.

Don't be afraid of "do not disturb."

Sometimes we just need a little peace and quiet to get things done, and that's okay! If placing your phone in another room doesn't stop the dings and pings from being heard while you need to get something done, you can simply set it on 'Do Not Disturb.' This will stop all notifications until you are ready to turn it off again. I do this every night.

Link your phone with your smartwatch. (If you like gizmos.)

Smart phones link up with smart watches. I have found this pretty helpful in recent years. Although I've said notifications can be a distracting part of my day, that doesn't mean I don't still need them! I like to keep my watch on me because not only does it track my steps when I'm out and about, but I can keep an eye on so many things with just a glance down.

Other Helpful Technology and Organization Tools

Use a password manager.

Your phone may have a built-in password tool that will autofill in your apps and logins for you. If you don't, think about downloading one; these are incredibly useful.

Read an eBook rather than a hardcopy.

Personally, I love a hardcopy of a book in my hands. But I know there are some that don't want to hassle of carrying around a paperback to the doctor's office or, if you're like my friends, are prone to leaving a book in unfortunate places and getting them wet, bent, run over, or torn. You can try the Kindle app on your phone. There are others, too.

Take your work on the go.

Whether you have your own business, you work from home for a company, or you have an office job, it's nice to know that if you take a day off or happen to be out of the office, you can still have all your files with you.

After freelancing for a while, I found it easier to have the documents I was working on also on my tablet or phone. That way, if I was in the doctor's office or waiting somewhere, I could be working on my projects if I got a new idea.

It also helps if you have a business where your employees are remote, or if you're just not keen on hopping on a Zoom call every time you need to discuss things. Most mobile apps give you a chat option, so that's a great advantage, as well. And I love the digital paper trail that online chats create.

I'll talk some more about paperless offices in the next section. For now, here are some business-on-the-go apps:

- Asana
- Slack
- Trello
- Workday
- Microsoft Teams

And don't forget the apps that let you take your files with you:

- IWork
- Microsoft Office Suite (Word, Excel, Powerpoint)
- OneDrive
- DropBox
- Office Suite
- Google Docs, Sheets, Slides, and Drive

Transitioning to the "paperless" office

Although this idea has been floating around for a while—and even implemented in a lot of places—I think the recent pandemic and the rise in remote work has brought it to everyone's attention tenfold. Not only is less paper good for the environment, but it is also a great gateway to those of us who are trying to be more organized.

Long gone are cabinets and file folders, we have scanners and online document storage! No more paper checks or money orders to pay our rent and other bills—we have auto drafts and online portals! W-2s are even accessible online now.

Here lately, I've been noticing a lot more electronic devices in offices and retail stores. I went for a visit to the hospital the other day and was given a tablet to sit down with and fill out the check in documents! It was quick and painless, and also a bit more sanitary, as they were able to wipe the iPad down as soon as I was done.

Benefits of the paperless office

1. Saves time
2. Saves space
3. Produces less waste
4. Bigger file storage
5. Easy access to storage
6. Better security (you hope)

All in all, the paperless office is the new wave. Do I think all paper is done for? Absolutely not. But it is hard to argue against the convenience of having most documents available with just a few clicks. If you're a 21st Century adult, you need to be working on living a life with a lot less paper.

Email Organization

One thing I had to come to terms with very quickly is that email organization is a daily task. Daily. Because of the influx of messages and information that we are sent in a span of twenty-four hours, it only makes sense that every time we do our morning check for updates, that we have to go through the process of weeding out what's important and what's not.

I try to set time aside in the beginning of my day and end of my day to check emails, that way I'm not distracting myself by checking on every ping of my inbox.

Another thing I learned is that the less you have to deal with, the quicker you can start to see your inbox as a place of productivity and organization. Which, as you should know from getting this far, begins with *decluttering*.

Exercise 56

Action step: When do you regularly assess your incoming email?

Where can you build in better email habits?

Write down your ideas as action statements.

Decluttering your inbox

Unsubscribe from the unnecessary.

I like to start with unsubscribing. This mostly goes for my personal email, because my business/work emails aren't necessarily riddled with coupons and ads for sales.

Unsubscribe to everything that you don't use on the regular—did you sign up for email reminders to Old Navy because of that one Christmas years ago you visited to get your mom a sweater? If it's likely you won't ever go back, unsubscribe.

Delete.

After you're done unsubscribing, (Okay, it's never really done is it?) it's time to move on to deleting what you don't need. This took me the most time because, as I mentioned earlier, I had quite a few emails stacked up in my inbox from a long period of neglect.

I have a personal email, a professional email, and a work email. So, I go through and try to figure out what's important in each one that I need to keep for the time-being. In personal, I delete old ads or coupons, reminders, newsletters, and spam.

In my work email, after I've solved any questions/concerns with clientele, I delete those messages because sometimes they hold personal information. I also try not to use my work email for anything that isn't work related, so I don't get anything confused. This also keeps it from piling up with things that aren't important!

Organizing your inbox

Now we'll move on to the next part—organization. Organizing emails can be kind of tricky to figure out, especially if you've got a bunch of different things coming in at once that don't necessarily fall under a single heading.

Create folders.

Folders have helped me sort out what needs to be done within a certain time frame. I have split my inbox into these categories:

- Inbox (my catch-all)
- Today
- This week
- This month

Exercise 57
Your thoughts: What sorting system do you use? Can it be improved? How?

Write down action statements.

Use priority inbox features.

Most email providers will offer you the option to set up your priority inbox. This inbox is where the types of emails you interact with the most will show up top, ahead of everything else that you might get.

In Gmail and other email platforms, it's usually determined based on the messages you open, who you chat with, and the content of the messages. To set it up, search in your email settings for something that says, "priority inbox" or "priority emails." This setting is also great for clearing up your phone notifications as well—it will only let you know when a priority email has come through, rather than alerting you of every new addition to your inbox.

Set up spam filters.

This saves me from the crazy amount of sorting that I had to do when I was first attempting to get my inbox under control.

I set this up by going into settings and playing around with what users I didn't want to receive emails from anymore. You can also set how aggressive your email provider is with filtering spam, which is a great tool as well.

146

Create a custom signature.

Along with organization, there are a few things you can do to make the process of replying a quicker experience! Set up your email signature in your settings. Mine has my name, business info, email, and telephone number.

Also, for information that is requested over and over (and over and over) I have created a "signature" with that information, and simply choose that signature when replying. Works great in the days just before an event when no-one has read the vendor instructions and each vendor emails me individually to ask the set-up hours!

Take advantage of pre-composed replies.

Pre-composed replies are gold! When you click reply, these will pop up at the bottom of your email as responses that the software thinks fit the situation—they're pretty accurate, too. I like to use these when I'm in a hurry on I'm on my phone instead of at my desk. You can also customize them if you tend to speak in less formal language than what they suggest.

Exercise 58

Your thoughts: Are there any replies you make often that could be converted to a custom signature?

Turn on Nudges.

Since I mostly use Gmail, I'll use it as my example here. Nudges are little taps on the shoulder to see if you may have forgotten something in your inbox—which is absolutely something I could use in real life, but alas, technology isn't *that* advanced yet.

If you've read a message and a day or two has went by without you sending a response, nudges will put that message at the front of your inbox and say something like, "This was sent to you 'x' days ago, do you want to reply now?"

In Outlook there is a daily update from Microsoft Viva. I ignored them at first, but when I started looking them over I found that Viva has a much better memory than I do. Then, at work, our industry-specific customer management software does the same thing...with all this going on, it is unlikely that I will be able to use the excuse, "It got lost in my in-box." Things are finding me now.

Paperless filing.

Going back to a few points I made earlier about the advantages of a paperless office—there's less paper, of course, but there's also less filing, less shuffling and moving around, and less searching.

Creating an online filing system may the key to getting rid of filing cabinets all together. (Okay, a fantasy, I know.) That is, if you can create a great, organized system that will help you easily locate what you need when you need it!

But...before you launch into a program of making all your papers digital, ask yourself if the papers in question are already digitized? Monthly utility statement? Probably available online! Retirement account statement? Online? Rules for your housing development? Probably online but hidden behind a member-only wall.

Your first task in organizing your paper digitally will be to create a master list of all your account numbers, usernames and passwords. Don't forget password managers we talked about earlier.

Exercise 59

Action step: Begin now to collect complete information on all your various account sign-ons. Start an Excel file, and every time you need to log onto a new site, add that information. (Or better yet, download a password manager app.)

But if you have done that, but still have papers you want to keep in electronic form, first things first—invest in the right equipment.

Scanners, copiers, and printers.

To get all of your papers onto the computer, you're going to need a copier, preferably with a scanner option built in. A printer combo is great as well—in case you need to print off, correct or sign any paperwork, and then upload it into your storage cloud.

If you are serious about digitizing your paper monster, remember how we address backlogs. Start from any paperwork you've gotten today and get it where you want it to be digitally. Once you've gotten a week or two under your belt (and in your digital files) start working backwards.

You want to start from most recent. When you make the decision to take your filing online, make sure to stick with it. You don't want to do it for a while or skip days, because that will surely cause a disruption and lot of lost/misplaced paperwork.

If there's a lot to be filed, try splitting it up into departments or getting your team to help you on a day-to-day basis. And remember to check and see if anything is already digitized! You don't need to digitize information that is already available electronically.

Online document sharers.

Having your documents in a file sharing site is absolutely essential if you have a team that is collaborating on a project.

Microsoft Teams has a great system for this and allows you to take advantage of Microsoft Office while you're in the program. You can create different projects and add team members in and restrict or give access to the files that you upload.

We've used Google Sheets and created a spreadsheet of everything needed for the annual family beach week. Everyone can go online and "claim" the items they are bringing to share. It helps avoid having 15 rolls of paper towels but no bathroom tissue.

Here are a few file sharing websites:

- Microsoft OneDrive
- Dropbox
- Google Drive
- Zippyshare
- Box
- Amazon Drive
- FileShare

Remember: only implement what is beneficial to you.

Some will find that a completely paperless office is just not attainable. You might have customers that prefer to sign in person on the dotted line rather than use e-signatures, or you may realize that some of your employees are still the pen and paper type rather than an iPad and iPencil type. It's okay to only take some of these to make your office more automated and organized—the point here is to figure out what works best for *you*.

Exercise 60

Your thoughts: What are some ways you can better use technology to make your life easier and less chaotic? Brainstorm and come up with ten ways to implement a technology solution.

1.

2.

3.

4.

5.

6.

7.

8.

9.

10.

Chapter Seventeen: Time Management

Yes, we all have 24 hours. But some of us have a lot more responsibilities than others. Admitting this difference is important. We shouldn't beat ourselves up when we seem to be forever behind. Instead, a better way to spend precious energy is to try to manage time well, eliminate anything that can be safely eliminated from our lives, and to set priorities.

Make time; don't wait for it. This concept applies to big dreams (becoming a screenwriter) and small chores (vacuuming the living room). If you wait until you have time, you probably won't accomplish your dream. If it is a chore, you'll do it at the last possible minute, do it poorly, and resent your efforts and the result. Make time.

Take advantage of the mini blocks of time in your life. (Remember the "One more thing" rule?) If you find yourself with 12 minutes to spare, draft a memo about the parking problem. If you see you have five minutes before you have to leave for work, start the dishwasher or a load of laundry. If you have 15 minutes, you can't tackle a whole project, but you can make a list of action steps and number them in priority order. You can return a phone call, address an envelope, and purge some files from your desk. Don't let this time go to waste.

Pare down. Ask yourself what you can jettison in your life. Can you resign from a committee you hate? Can you eliminate your answering machine, thereby relieving yourself of having to return phone calls? (It leaves the ball in the caller's court.) Can you decide to never again buy Dry Clean Only clothes? Decide not to do the things that have been on your To-Do list for more than a month, or a year--whatever time frame makes you realize it is not a critical item.

Exercise 61

Your thoughts: What are your biggest time issues?

Now, on to how to organize your time:

Spend some time each week planning the entire week— not just your day. What are the major accomplishments you need to see this week? Schedule them day by day. Include your personal tasks, too. Use your calendar and note on each day the things you need to accomplish that day.

Figure in the complexity of your tasks. This is especially pertinent when you are setting priorities and ranking what you want to accomplish. Are you waiting for input from six other people? That factor may increase the time required for this task— thus making it merit a longer span of time in your schedule. A committee of three can work faster than a committee of nine.

Conduct a time inventory. If you feel like you are spinning your wheels, it can be helpful to what you spend most of your attention and energy on. On a sheet of paper, jot down the time you turn your attention to a task, along with a one- or two-word description of the task. Each time you change tasks, note the time and the new activity. This tool will help you see the structure (or lack thereof) of a day in your life. It may also help you identify timewasters and eliminate them.

Consider negative impacts. To set priorities when you just can't identify the greater importance of any one of a number of seemingly equally important tasks, try considering the negative consequences of not accomplishing each one. The one with the greatest negative impact may then become your top priority. Consider here the life-style negative impact — such as daily aggravation, as well as the threat of being fired.

Develop a mission statement. Determine what it is you are trying to accomplish, and then do only those things that move you toward the completion of the project your mission statement describes.

Do the hardest (or yuckiest) part of a task first. That way your dread of the yuck won't stop you from proceeding. I've spent days dreading a task, only to complete it in a matter of minutes.

Keep lists. These can consist of tasks, things to buy, or measurements for things you need. Then, when you have that extra mini block of time, you can glance at your list and decide what to tackle next.

Mark essential blocks of time on your calendar. Keep track of how much time you might need for planning, resting, housekeeping, etc. Give yourself the same priority as you would someone else. Schedule it.

Exercise 62:

Your thoughts: Which of the above suggestions will help you the most?

1.

2.

3.

4.

Action step: Develop a timeline or method to implement each one.

What will challenge you the most? Why?

Chapter Eighteen: Procrastination

I have found that people have to really drill down into procrastination in their lives to honestly assess its impact before they can address it. As long as they blind themselves to the truth, procrastination is just a difficult habit to break. And habits do sound harmless, inconsequential. But a well-developed habit of procrastination can seriously lower the quality of your life.

You've heard of writer's block, haven't you? That inexplicable malady that causes words and thoughts to vanish when faced with an empty page? That's closely akin to action-block.

You have action-block when you know you need to do something. You have to do it. There's no getting around it, but you don't do it. Instead, you just dread it. This form of procrastination leads to action-block, which in turn seems to manifest itself in the back of your mind as dread. I've dreaded things so much and so long that when I finally got around to doing them, it was a relief. In fact, I've spent more time and energy dreading a task than the task itself takes. Boy. What a waste!

Before we start discussing action-block busters, we need to really address all sides of procrastination. Sure, it causes undue dread, sleepless nights and may be even stress-induced heartburn. But you know what? It sometimes works!

In my career as a librarian, I've seen procrastination in all its forms. One especially upsetting version includes the over-involved parent: the scenario when I have seen a parent actually doing their child's research. Tah-dah! The child's procrastination worked big time. He didn't want to do the research. He put it off, and out of the blue a rescuer (frequently mom or a girlfriend) saves the day. The sad truth is, sometimes procrastination pays off.

On some tasks, if you procrastinate long enough, the need to complete the task just fades away. Put off doing the paperwork for a rebate and the rebate is void. Manufacturers actually count on folks doing this.

Graduate school? The long and tedious application process must be complete by March 1st; delay long enough and there won't be enough time to get the paperwork done. A side benefit here is you don't have to deal with possible rejection if you "don't have enough time" to apply. Procrastination is a good cover for plain old fear.

This leads us to another way procrastination pays off: If you do everything at the last minute, you can always blame lack of time for a sub-par or mediocre job. It is not you, you tell yourself. You're not really a "C" student; you just didn't give yourself enough time to write the "A" paper you know you are capable of. Having an explanation (lack of time) is useful to a lot of people.

Exercise 63

Your thoughts: Everyone procrastinates. What are your problem areas? List them below.

Are there any positives that arise fromm procrastination?

What are the negatives? List some.

Despite the few ways procrastination "works," though, it has far more negative consequences than positive ones. From late fees to friendly little chats with the IRS, procrastination can keep you in hot water with a lot of people—from your spouse to your boss. It is not a peaceful way to live.

Let's talk ourselves out of this bad habit. First, drop the myth that you work better under pressure. Study after study has shown that you simply don't. Students who start their research projects sooner make far better grades than those who wait till the last minute. "But that's not a fair comparison. You're comparing an A project that took three weeks to a C project that took three hours!" complained one of my students.

Using your own "I do better under pressure" argument, that C paper would have been a D or F if started three weeks earlier. You don't really believe that do you?

The truth is when we are under pressure, stressed out and tired, we don't perform our best. Adrenaline can take the human mind and body only so far. And if you live on a perpetual diet of adrenaline, you probably become somewhat dulled to its performance-boosting properties.

To further beat the "better under pressure" myth into the ground, consider this fact. College students who procrastinate report much higher levels of stress and are more likely to develop colds and other illnesses by the time finals roll around. Ever attempted a calculus final with a fever and runny nose? I'll bet it is not a pretty sight.

Procrastinators simply invite more stress into their lives. They invite guilt over things not done, gifts never purchased, letters never written. It does not make for a peaceful existence.

Exercise 64

Your thoughts: Have you ever believed that you work better under pressure? Was your work really superior?

How could not procrastinating make you more effective?

Action-block busters.

Here are some strategies to help you break through procrastination. Use them in combination with one another.

Break down the task you are procrastinating on into steps. If it is a large project, your steps may be broken down even further. Don't do this task in your mind. Do it on paper. Spend some time listing all the steps, no matter how mundane.

Trick yourself into starting the task. There's an expression we use in my part of the country. It is "I'm fixing to" do something. Note that the speaker isn't actually indicating a start to the task; rather he or she is indicating a willingness to prepare to start to do the task.

"I'm fixing to go to prayer meeting" may involve a change of clothes, a shower or whipping up a dessert to take along. When someone is fixing to get ready to go, you don't go crank up the car. You might be an hour away from leaving.

How does this help cure action-block? Easy--it sets the stage and helps reveal how simple the task is.

If you are "fixing to " to write a report you might do these things-

Get some paper

Boot up your computer

Gather your notes

Pull together the information you have

Go gather some additional information

Brew some coffee

When you've done all these things, no one's said you have to start writing. You're just "fixed" to go. But, once all these things are done, it is far easier to start the project. You don't have to start it—just put your list of steps on top of the notepad you've lain out—or lean it up against the monitor. You may even discover you've done some of the steps.

And if you've started completing the steps, you're not procrastinating anymore.

If dreading a task is sapping your energy, try breaking the task into steps and evaluating each step. Which ones do you really dread?

Figure this out and get those out of the way first. You may find your desire to procrastinate is gone, once you've eliminated the parts that you liked least or dreaded most. I love having parties. But the task I dread the most—addressing the invitations-- can really stop me in my tracks.

If I can make myself sit down and address them—every one—even the ones where I have to look up the zip code—then everything else is a piece of cake. Polishing silver, no big deal. Cleaning up, not a problem. Everything is easier once I've finished the task I like the least.

And it is important I do all of it—all the way to locating missing zip codes. If I do everything but "the hard ones," the task still hangs in the back of my mind nagging me.

What about delegating a dreaded task? If you've procrastinated on the same type of task—say arranging committee meetings—maybe there's someone else in your organization (or household) who could do it better.

You could always pay someone to do the things you put off. Hate tax forms? Find an accountant. Gutters haven't been cleaned out in, oh, forever? Hire someone to do it.

Some tasks you procrastinate on can simply be deleted from your "to do" list. Just be prepared to accept the consequences gracefully. If you decide to give up on the gutters and leave them clogged with debris year-round, put aside some money for repair bills. Or spend money now on high-quality gutter guards so you don't have to worry about it.

You might want to bargain with yourself. If you accomplish the dreaded task, you'll celebrate by doing something you wouldn't otherwise. Rewards tend to work better than punishments.

We can tell ourselves, "If I don't pay bills tonight, I won't watch [whatever show you're currently addicted to]." But often we procrastinate on a task, say, paying bills, and then watch the TV show anyway. So, think of a reward that's really a reward. It is important that it be something you wouldn't do otherwise, or you'll just procrastinate and treat yourself anyway.

Gather witnesses! Tell other people that you are about to attack the dreaded task. Better yet, ask them to hold you accountable. I've told my co-workers "I've got a deadline. If you see me outside my office for more than a restroom break—send me back to work." This technique can be really effective.

Schedule time for the task—officially—in your date book. By blocking out time you address one of your biggest excuses: No time.

Just do it. Nike says it best. Stop talking, thinking about it, agonizing over it, dreading it, complaining about it—just do it. The mere act of starting may be what it takes to break through your action-block.

Apply the Pareto Principle. You might not have to break 100% of your procrastination habits. Focus on the areas where the habit causes you the most negativity. Are you always later, making family, friends and co-workers angry? Find out where procrastination hurts the most and decide to address those.

Or Don't Apply the Pareto Principle!

Use the credit card snowball technique. Have you ever heard about paying off your smallest balance first (no matter what the interest rate on the card), and then when that one is paid off, roll that money into paying off the next smallest balance? This is helpful because of the psychological reward of seeing balances paid completely off. It's a win. A success. If you think you might be in need of such a boost, work on correcting a tiny procrastination problem first. Nail it. Celebrate it. Now you know you can beat the big P. Use that momentum to tackle the next challenge.

Keep it up. If you've been a severe, lifelong procrastinator, you are not likely to break the habit in a day or two. Tell yourself " I am going to stop procrastinating," and then, task-by-task, work through the bad habit. It is probably not helpful to say, "I'll never, ever procrastinate again" when you know that future procrastination is likely. That's setting yourself up for failure and gives legs to defeatist self-talk. "There, I've procrastinated again—I'm doomed. I'll never get out of this." That kind of "all-or-nothing" thinking is a hindrance to overcoming procrastination. Instead, tell yourself "I'm procrastinating less and less every day. I'm getting better about not putting things off."

Before long, you'll be living proof that action-block does not have to be a chronic malady.

Exercise 65

Your thoughts: List below your top three procrastination areas you want to address.

1.

2.

3.

Review the advice you just read in the previous section.

Write down some steps you can take to address the three areas you noted above.

1.

2.

3.

Exercise 66

Using a separate piece of paper—develop a plan and timeline to address each of your three priority areas.

Hint: You can use the format of the Goal Setting worksheets from the beginning of the Workbook.

Chapter Nineteen: Systems or Organization on Autopilot

The best forms of organization are those that lead to consistently and painlessly accomplishing a routine task. Here are some tasks that lend themselves to "automatic" organization if you set up a method of accomplishing it and then do it until it becomes a habit.

Paying bills

Keeping a Family Master Calendar

Keeping a personal calendar

Keeping an address book

Tracking household needs

Sorting incoming mail

Processing email

Handling voice mail

How do you get tasks to work easily?

1. *Keep it simple.* If you make it too complicated, it won't work. I have simple "systems" for dealing with certain items around the house. Everything to do with "light" is in a certain cupboard—flashlights, candles, matches, spare batteries, and even extra light bulbs are all kept in one place. I never have to think about where I might have stashed spare bulbs or a flashlight. A grocery list is stuck to the fridge at all times. If I were to conceal it in a pretty

basket or inside a cupboard, we'd seldom use it. This is making "point of use" a priority.

2. **Make it consistent.** Keeping like things together, for instance, is logical and systematic. I keep all our vases on one shelf in our laundry room. I never have to wonder where a vase is. It is either out on display or on this shelf. I have determined places for almost everything in our house. If you know how to manage a magical disappearing cat, please advise!

3. **Employ the Point of Use principle.** Consider placing items needed as you leave the house near the door, for example. We have a large, ugly heavy-duty coat rack right by the door. This is where I hang dog leashes, umbrellas, hats and coats. When I have to make sure I take an item to work, I often put it in a handle bag and hang it on this rack. Even when I don't need to grab a coat, I can still see the bag in plain view. If something is super-critical, I hang in on the door. Or better still, put my car keys in with the item I am trying to remember. (Although this still gives me a start, when I feel in my outermost pocket and find no keys!

It is best to try to keep frequently used items "one reach" away. If you use certain kitchen tools when at the stove, consider keeping them in a jar or crock right on the stovetop or adjacent counter. That way you don't have to reach once to open a drawer, a second time to get the needed implement and a third time to close the drawer.

In my kitchen, items used daily are in the lower overhead cabinets. In my laundry room, I leave the box of soap out in plain view. We consume a lot of rice, so it is kept in a canister on the kitchen counter, even though we know that most people use the largest canister in a set for sugar or flour.

4. *Group things in a single location.* I keep envelopes, return address labels and stamps all in one place. I keep all my "morning" vitamins and medicines in the kitchen, where I eat my breakfast, and my "evening" supplements in the bathroom drawer. I am much more likely to actually take my vitamins this way.

At work, I have a worktable in my office upon which I keep scissors, tape, paper clips, a stapler, pens and pencils, as well as some 3M sticky notes. These materials are actually duplicates of items I keep in my desk drawer, but when I use the table for meetings or to spread out a project, it is very convenient to have everything I need at hand. These supplies are also stashed in ceramic cups that seem to multiply all over the office and kept on a two handled tray. I can pick up and move to the next room easily.

For other types of projects, I use large file folders with accordion pleated sides. The trick is that I not only keep the papers I'm working on here, but also three-dimensional objects that will fit as well. I might stuff in markers and nametag badges along with handouts to take to a meeting or class. I might put a stack of papers, a book or two, and a pad of 3M sticky notes to use for jotting down ideas as I review a manuscript or article. I've even been known to slip a small bottle of aspirin into a file, when I'm taking it to a taxing meeting. The point is, I am able to "bunch" things by topic, and not have to scrounge around for needed items every time I turn to a project.

And one last extreme example? We have metal strips on the inside of our pantry where clips go to hold shelves. When I had leftovers after a pantry re-do, I got a large staple gun and stapled the packet of remaining clips inside the pantry. Now I'll never have to look again!

5. *Create coding systems.* I keep all files relating to money in green files. Household files are blue. With laundry, it is helpful to code kids' clothes. One system I know of dealt with the issue of hand-me-downs very well. The oldest son had no markings on his clothes. When an item became outgrown and was passed on the second son, a single black dot was added in an inconspicuous place. In the cases where the item lasted until the third son could use it, a second dot was added to the first. These dots were also used on new clothes purchased for the boys to make sorting easier. My husband, the first son in this scenario, had re-inherited clothing as his brothers got older. I was really wondering why his white socks had dots on the toes when we met.

The key to using systems to make your life easier is to keep them simple. The best system in the world, if it is too complicated to implement, isn't very useful at all. In our coding example, if the mother of the boys decided to buy cute, embroidered labels with each of the boys' names on them, she'd have to first order them, then apply them with a sewing machine, and finally change them when the item got bumped down a son. A system that is that time consuming is likely to fall by the wayside when life gets busy.

Exercise 67

Your thoughts: Do you have systems in place for many of your daily activities? List some.

Think of two or three activities you engage in regularly that could benefit from developing a system to deal with that activity. List below.

1.

2.

3.

For each, determine what you need to develop a system.

Choose one of these items and develop a system and set it up. Right now. Really. Just go do it.

Chapter Twenty: Your Closet

To show how the principles or organization apply to household areas, let's apply the principles to something we all have (and most of us dread): our closets. Closets are a good starting point because everybody has one, and most likely, it is the source of at least some dissatisfaction. If you haven't already conquered your closet, let's tackle it this week.

Do you often peer into your closet, but find little to wear? While your problem may be a legitimate shopping issue (you don't have enough clothes), it is a hundred times more likely to be an organization and thinking problem. It is an organization problem because you use your closet inefficiently. It is a thinking problem because your attitude about clothes may need adjustment.

As always, the beginning step is to critically examine the contents of your closet and discard the items that are simply unnecessary.

Remember the principles:

If in doubt, throw it out. If you're unsure about an item, toss it. A test for this decision is hesitation. The real "keepers" are instantly obvious. When you have to use your imagination to think of when you might wear something again, odds are 100 to 1 that it is a toss item. Plan to go through your closet and evaluate every item for donation to Goodwill or the Salvation Army.

Use it or lose it. If you haven't worn it in over a year, consider letting it go. If you're like most of us—by the time an event comes around to wear it, the style will be out, or your waist will be out!

Recycle. Is there a better person or place for this item? Goodwill maybe? Can this item be altered to be more stylish? Or is it fit only to be turned into a rag? Will you take the trouble to see that it happens?

Set limits. How many navy sports coats does one person need? Ditto for white shirts. Even the basics like "the classic black dress" can be overdone if the owner has an entire collection. For true basics, consider a limit—such as one short black skirt and one long black skirt.

Do one more thing. When you take something out of your closet or return it to the closet, take the time to do it right. Return hangers to an appropriate place. When re-hanging clothes, insure they are wearable for the next use. Check for soiling and possible mending needs. To make your life even easier, when tossing things into the hamper, go ahead and unbutton those tiny button-down collar buttons. Check the pockets for forgotten items. (Washed and dried lip balm can be deadly to clothes.)

A place for everything. When arranging your closet, keep like items together. Keep all jackets in one section, all slacks in another. All button-down shirts together. (I sort mine by color.) I even go as far as to have all my sleeveless shirts together, all my short-sleeved items together, etc.

Don't collect junk. If your closets are bulging, be a snob. Keep only the items that are well made and flatter you. If you feel yucky every time you wear an ensemble, by all means, send it on to Goodwill.

Exercise 68

Action step: Make an appointment with yourself to address your closet.

I will spend time sorting, purging and organizing my closet on _____.
Add this to your calendar.

Is this a multi-hour project? Multi-day? Plan accordingly.

What supplies will you need? Boxes, bags? Make a list.

Of you have items that are ready to be passed along, where will you take them? Jot that down.

What are the operating hours of the donation center you plan to donate to? Look it up and write it down.

How do you think you will feel once you have disposed of items you no longer need? Why?

A Good Defense Is Proactive Shopping: If in Doubt, Don't Buy It.

When you shop for clothes, become highly proactive. All along you've asked yourself if the item matched the rest of your wardrobe. Now consider these other questions:

Is this machine washable? If you rarely go to the dry cleaners, the item will wind up soiled and stored for weeks in a heap waiting for you to get around to having it cleaned. I've had students in my organization class report outfits going out of style in the time it took to get around to dry-cleaning them.

Does this fit my lifestyle? Is it an item that you will wear repeatedly? Even for "special events" clothes, try to get versatile items. For example, if you're in the market for a classic, black cocktail dress, think in terms of one that will also serve as funeral attire. If you get the ultra-slinky, sexy dress that's only for parties, you'll still need another dark dress for the more somber events. Consider an in-between dress that can be made festive with "statement" accessories or toned down.

Will I need to alter this item? If you have a poor track record for actually getting alterations done, keep shopping.

How much will this cost per use? This question is a way of considering clothing purchases that will foster the purchase of high-quality, high-use items. For example, if you are considering a basic black belt, and you know you will wear it several times a week for several years, you can then justify spending more for higher quality leather. On the other hand, if the item has a trendy look that you suspect may be not trendy in a year, you will want to pay less for it as it will have far fewer wearings. When considered this way, a $150 pair of dark shoes are a much better value than they may first appear. Well-maintained, they might wind up costing mere pennies per use.

The old standbys—Does this item fit well and flatter me? Does it feel good on?

Remember, no matter how good the sale, it is money wasted if you never wear the item.

Transitional and Special Occasion Clothing Storage Tips

Swap your clothing as the seasons change. Have you ever gone a full year without really swapping your clothes? You just keep going back to the spare closet to take out one more outfit. After about ten months, your "active" closet is crammed, and your spare closet has only things you can no longer wear, or wouldn't be caught dead in.

Each spring, put away your winter clothes and bring out your warm weather wardrobe. Swap them out in the fall. Okay, we know you'll have to leave out some outfits for those strangely cool or warm days but put away the bulk of your one-season clothes. If you find you went all winter without wearing some of the winter clothes, it sounds like a Goodwill donation to me.

When switching your wardrobe, inventory your clothes. Thinking about the proactive shopping tips, critically decide which (if any) of the "Goodwill" candidates need to be replaced. Are your favorite items showing wear and in need of replacement? If you shop proactively and only for specific needed items, it may take a while to find the exact item you need to replace. This is where that smart phone list will come in handy.

It is also very important to ensure the clothes you store are absolutely clean and ready for storage. Have you ever found money in the pocket of an item you took out of storage? I once stored a white linen dress with a colored paper napkin in the pocket. When I took it out the next spring, the color of the napkin had transferred itself to the dress, ruining it. Even if clothes look clean, colorless "stains" can darken over time. If in doubt, re-clean an item, if you're positive you want to keep it.

Exercise 69

Your thoughts: Is a seasonal wardrobe swap a feasible practice for you? Why or why not?

What are the benefits of implementing a seasonal clothing swap, if any?

Chapter Twenty-One: Home Organization

First off, it is going to be work. The "workless house" is about as likely to arrive as the "paperless" office. I mean, it's coming...but at a glacier's pace. Better organization will reduce your household workload but will not eliminate it.

Exercise 70

Your thoughts: What areas of your home would you like to address?

The first step in household organization: de-cluttering.

Before organizing an area, first purge the area. Remember, my favorite principle of organization: If in doubt, throw it out. If you begin to organize before you've eliminated the excess inventory, you'll waste precious energy rearranging items that really belong in the donation bin.

Remove clutter first and then organize. Ask yourself: Why am I reorganizing Mason Jars and lids when I haven't canned in 30 years and don't even have so much as a tomato plant in my yard?

Here are some concrete tips based on the ten principles that will help make your household more manageable.

Make daily pick-up a routine.

Thinking of the "One More Thing" principle, go ahead and spend 15 to 20 minutes doing a quick walk-through of your home, collecting old newspapers, stray dishes, and odd shoes and socks that get dispersed everywhere. If you do this once for each room daily, your house will always be moderately presentable. It won't be dusted, but you'll have a place to sit, should company drop in.

Make this a routine you perform each day, and you'll never find yourself buried under three weeks' debris. If you have de-cluttered each room, it should be much easier to keep things in their places.

A place for everything: even parking places.

Create "parking places" in each room for things that don't really belong permanently in that room, but that you are using there for the time being. Think gift wrapping supplies around Christmas. I wind up with small stacks of books in the den, baskets into which I toss magazines we're still reading, and so on. By limiting the space devoted to these items, they never take over, and if I want to read the current issue of Southern Living, I know it is in the stack in the basket. By using attractive parking spaces—baskets, decorative boxes, and even space on shelves, these items can be kept at hand without adding clutter to a room.

Don't collect junk.

Keep a critical eye on what you add to your surroundings. Imagine a visitor walking through your front door into your living room. What would you like the visitor to know about you by what is seen? That you love books or penguins? Do you want the image presented to be calming and soothing or energetic and fun loving? Decide these things about each room in your home, and de-clutter as appropriate.

A big issue at this point is the reality of living in your home. If you have two separate living areas, perhaps you can justify snow-white carpet and upholstered furniture in the formal living room. But if you really have to use these items, purchase colors and materials that suit your lifestyle. If you're going to be a nervous wreck every time you have company for fear someone will spill something on your beautiful rug, you'll soon stop entertaining. Maybe you need a different rug.

The most beautiful things in the world, if they are simply not functional, just become another category of high-class junk. I referred to it earlier as junque. It still may not belong in your life.

Set limits.

If the number one cause of disorganization is postponed decisions, a close second is just too much stuff. We have too much stuff in our closets, drawers, pantries, and cupboards. We can't find the things we need, so we assume we're out and we go buy more, only to discover later that we already had the item hidden behind fourteen other things. Set limits. No one says you can't keep some paper bags on hand. But there should be a very real limit on the number you keep. (Keep only the amount that fits into a single paper bag, for example.)

Remember the point of use principle.

I keep Windex™ in my bathroom closet because that's what I use on the bathroom mirror. I also keep it in the kitchen because I use it on the counters and also on the floor in the event of minor spills. Try to keep household items where you need them. Everything to do with laundry should be stored in the laundry room.

Determine a place for everything.

For some items, you'll need to pick a single location where they will be kept. It may not be ideal—but it needs to be definite. I keep all our light bulbs in a drawer in the dining room. Not logical, but it is consistent—all light bulbs are there—even the little, tiny ones that go in the night lights.

In our kitchen we have two spaces where we keep spices. Baking spices (used rarely) are in one place, while the regular cooking spices are one reach away from the stovetop. I keep party supplies way up high on the top shelf of a cabinet. I have to get a ladder to get them down. No big deal—we don't have parties every day—but I keep all that stuff together. So, it's one stop shopping to see what's on hand and take it down.

Having pre-approved placement for almost everything in the house is very helpful. And my placement is not super-specific. I keep "party supplies" in a single location—that's everything from snazzy napkins to serving trays. I don't have to think of separate places for platters, party paper products, and chafing pans.

Bonus principle: If in doubt, don't buy it.

Buy the simplest appliance to meet the most of your needs. If you really think you are going to heat up frozen pizza more than once or twice a month, maybe, just maybe, the pizza zapper is right for you. But I sort of doubt it. In most cases the oven works fine. Do you need a vegetable steamer, when a saucepan will do the same thing and take up less space? You can use the saucepan all the time. An electric steamer you use only to steam; the other 322 days of the year when you do not steam vegetables, the steamer is sitting there, in the way, consuming space.

Marketers today are really good at combining items to invent new products. But I'd think twice before buying a complicated combination appliance when a simpler one will do. The simpler one is easier to operate and probably has fewer parts to lose or break.

If you are on the verge of buying a new appliance or gadget, ask yourself how often you will use it versus the space, time and energy it will take up. While I have an electric can opener (a gift from my parents) we almost never use it because my 1930s kitchen counter space is very scarce. I hate to devote almost a square foot to an electric can opener when I can keep a hand model in a drawer, one reach away. The big electric can opener is kept under the sink for when I have a large number of cans to open—say, when making a huge batch of red beans and rice. I still use it, but not enough to justify giving it top value space.

Closed storage [usually] looks better than open storage in real life.

Beautiful glass front cabinets are lovely in the glossy decorating magazines that barrage us from grocery store checkout lines. But the truth is, unless you are very disciplined about putting things away very neatly every time, it may not look so great in your home. I do have some glass front cupboards in my kitchen. Luckily, I have monochrome dishes (all edges are white) and a collection of clear glassware for my everyday use. I do have about three red items, tasting bowls and a mug my dad gave me to add visual interest. But believe me, anything I even think of adding to this cabinet is either clear or white. If I went to cheerful colors, I'd have to keep it a whole lot neater. As it is, the simple color palette makes up for a lot.

Use colors to create organization.

Most of us don't think of color as an organizing tool, unless it is associated with a coding schedule. But color can be used to greatly enhance your organization. Here are some easy ways. At home, I have limited our linen colors. We have only white and sage bathroom towels. The white towels go in the guest bath, and the sage ones in the master bath. The color alone provides the "sort" key. And the look of a monochrome closet is especially pleasing to the eye. Any closet with a single color or narrow color palette looks neater than a closet with a riot of colors. Notice in upscale catalogues that show home and closet organizers that most of the clothes are neutral colors, and very few colors at that. It just looks neater.

However, if you are a person who likes a pop of color in their wardrobe, you can always keep your basics neutral and have your outerwear or other accessories add a little spice to your wardrobe. I keep my work blouses in white, black, and beige so that when I throw on my favorite mustard cardigan for fall, I'm not mixing too many colors or patterns!

Besides bath towels, I've applied this color-organization principle to other linens throughout the house. Kitchen towels are red. Master bed sheets are ecru. The powder room hand towels are multi-colored. All linens are stored in the room where they are used. Thus, a stray hand towel can be easily spotted and returned to its home.

I use these same limits on colors when purchasing household supplies. All paper towels are plain white, as is facial tissue (in green boxes, if possible). By limiting colors present, rooms appear less cluttered and more spacious. I have even been known to select shampoo because I liked the color of the bottle. Sounds extreme, but the fewer colors to clamor for your eye's attention, the more serene a space appears.

Exercise 71

Action step: List your top three household organization priorities.

1.

2.

3.

Using the following pages (which will look familiar) develop a plan to address them.

Household Organization Goal Number One

My goal is:

Supplies Needed:

Systems I need to develop:

My deadline for accomplishment is:

Here are the steps I can take to meet this goal:

Time Frame	Action or Step

A reward I can give myself for accomplishing this goal is:

Some positive outcomes I will enjoy are:

Household Organization Goal Number Two

My goal is:

Supplies Needed:

Systems I need to develop:

My deadline for accomplishment is:

Here are the steps I can take to meet this goal:

Time Frame	Action or Step

A reward I can give myself for accomplishing this goal is:

Some positive outcomes I will enjoy are:

Household Organization Goal Number Three

My goal is:

Supplies Needed:

Systems I need to develop:

My deadline for accomplishment is:

Here are the steps I can take to meet this goal:

Time Frame	Action or Step

A reward I can give myself for accomplishing this goal is:

Some positive outcomes I will enjoy are:

Chapter Twenty-Two: Housework

Very few people look forward to housecleaning. In spite of this aversion, some housekeeping does need to get done for your home to be presentable and comfortable (especially when your parents, in-laws or boss are visiting). And while we're talking about it, why only get your house in order when company's coming? Why not enjoy a peaceful, organized home yourself? Here are some ideas about how to keep housework from taking over your life.

First, de-clutter. This step may take a while, but the payoff justifies the work. Besides, de-cluttering your home may in itself make your home look cleaner.

Plan to de-clutter first. If you jump into organizing, you'll just be organizing stuff you won't keep. If you try to clean first, you'll spend a lot of energy cleaning things you will later remove.

De-cluttering a home (use the directions in chapter seven) is a big task and not one that should be attempted unless there is a block of time sufficient to do some good. When you work at de-cluttering your home, start small. Pick a linen closet. You want something definite, with clear boundaries, that is manageable for the time you have to devote to it. If you have three days, tackle the garage. If you have 30 minutes, do the junk drawer in the kitchen.

Once you have de-cluttered, you are ready to organize. You may be tempted to jump straight into cleaning, but with the exception of perhaps wiping down a shelf before you return its rightful contents, don't.

Exercise 73

Action step: Create a declutter schedule and put it on your calendar.

What's the difference between cleaning and organizing? Organization happens to look a lot like cleaning—and the results appear to be similar—a neater, more presentable area.

The difference is the underlying issue. The issue with cleaning is dirt, a physical manifestation of "yuck." The underlying issue with disorganization is mental: postponed decisions, bad habits, excess "stuff," or maybe even laziness.

When you clean, you address dirt. When you organize you address behavior as well as the physical arrangement of items in a space. Organization is definitely the more important of the two. You can easily clean an organized space. You can also easily organize a dirty space. But cleaning a disorganized space is very difficult. It is hard to get at the dirt when everything is in utter chaos.

Once you have de-cluttered, focus on organizing and setting up systems to maintain the organization. Set up an incoming mail sorting system, a system to pay bills, a system to track projects and all assorted pieces.

Why do all these things first? Because your time is important, and you'll spend far less time cleaning an organized space.

After you've de-cluttered, organized and begun deep cleaning, you'll want your house to stay that way. How? You put it on a schedule.

Did I mention a calendar as a housekeeping tool? It should be counted among the dust rags and cleansers, for it is just as important. We'll talk about a master calendar shortly, but for now know that figuring out a schedule for your housekeeping is critical. Some things are done daily— others weekly, others seasonally—and a good schedule will help keep you from forgetting and letting tings slide so long they become catastrophic.

Does this sound dreadful? Think of this as a way to buy time when you need it. You won't ever have to waste a terrific fall Saturday on housework if you've accomplished it in bits and pieces through the week.

Exercise 74

Your thoughts: Do you feel you spend too much of your free time on household tasks?

Would becoming and staying organized help speed up housekeeping or reduce the need for it?

What are some things you can tell yourself to motivate you to do more small things daily so you'll have less to do on your days off?

Don't forget the "one more thing principle."

If there is only one principle to remember when considering housework, it is the "One More Thing" principle. How many times do you rush off to another task before completing the task you're on? I know you remember to turn off the stove. But why not go ahead and put those last few dirty dishes in the dishwasher? Doing one more thing before you move on to the next task will ensure that when you return, things will be a little more in order. Continual employment of this principle will train you to do mini "pickups" all throughout your day, with the result being a home that doesn't get quite as out of hand as it could. Train your family members to do these things as well.

Often your one more thing will be to use one of the other principles you're learning, such as "Handle It Once" or "Determine a Place for Everything." Try it for a week. You'll be surprised how much time you eventually save when you spend a few minutes proactively dealing with chaos before it spirals out of control.

Exercise 75

Action step: choose one principle to focus on for a week. I will use the

_____

Principle in as many ways possible this week,

How do you think this will help?

After one week do a self-check. Did you employ your chosen principle as often as possible?

What was the result?

End the quest for perfection

I'm a recovering perfectionist. Perfectionism used to keep me worn out. Mop the kitchen floor? I'd do it until it was surgical-suite clean. It still got dirty in between and even though it was clean enough to eat off of, no one did so but the dog. But my perfectionism wouldn't let me simply do an adequate job and move on. I wasted a lot of time on my kitchen floor.

Have you ever decided to straighten up the house, only to wind up deep cleaning one room while the rest of the house remains in shambles? If it is spring-cleaning time for you, fine. But if you were just trying to tidy up on Sunday evening in order to get ready for the week, and you spent six hours cleaning the bathroom only to fall into bed before getting the laundry done, you'll wake up Monday with no clean clothes, despite the pristine bathroom.

Surrender the goal of perfection. Does Martha Stewart ever stop by your house? Probably not. So put away your visions of Martha Stewart-like perfection and settle for a household standard that leaves you time and energy for the things you find important—perhaps eating better, exercising more, or simply enjoying life.

Our goal for housework is somewhere along the lines of "Clean enough that I enjoy living in my house," or the way I like to phrase it "Fifteen minutes from company." a.m. I ready for company at all times? No, but if someone dropped by, I could open the door and invite them in. But if they called and said, "I'm on my way," in 15 minutes I'd be ready for almost anyone, except perhaps Martha Stewart.

It is not perfect. But it is peaceful enough that I enjoy being home. That'll do.

Here's how I deal with a latent perfectionist tendency. I set a kitchen timer, and tell myself, "I'll spend five minutes on this shower enclosure. When the timer rings, I rinse and move on. Funny—five minutes of cleaning looks a lot like 20 minutes' worth.

Exercise 76

Your thoughts: Of the spectrum from perfection to sloth, where do you feel you fall?

Do you want to change this?

Why?

List three ways adapting in this area could give you more peace of mind.

1.

2.

3.

Listen to the experts.

Read *Speedcleaning* by Jeff Campbell. Jeff does house cleaning for a living, and he's made a science of doing it fast. He has tons of information about how to do the job and what type of cleaner or equipment to do it with. This book is perhaps my favorite housework book. (It is also short and very entertaining—plus it presents a master plan on involving other family members in the cleaning process.)

Laundry blues.

If you really don't like laundry, avoid it like the plague! Okay—I know you have to have nice clothes to wear to work and church—but try to think "laundry avoidance" whenever possible.

Play clothes are a lot easier to wash and fold than "dress" clothes. So, teach your children to change their clothes before going outside to play. Teach your partner the same thing! When you get home, change immediately—and check your clothes and either re-hang them is wearable, or put them in the laundry basket. Apply stain treatment now if needed.

Remember our little pep talk about perfectionism? **Think about lowering your standards when it comes to laundry.** In our household, the only items we religiously wash after each use are underwear, socks and T-shirts.

If you do laundry at home, **pick your laundry days and stick to them.** If something "misses" the hamper and doesn't get washed, too bad—it'll have to wait for the next laundry day. I use this simple rule and have determined that my laundry day is Sunday. So, on Sundays when family obligations keep me busy visiting relatives and such, my husband knows that I won't have as much time to do laundry. If he accepts multiple commitments, I may not even get to the laundry. In that case, he waits (or does his own).

My record for not having a free Sunday was about four weeks. By the end of the four weeks, we were wearing some interesting outfits—but amazingly we had enough underclothes and socks to go that long. We didn't die for lack of clean laundry.

Clean out your closets! Cleaner, sparer closets also mean that your fresh clothing won't be crammed and stuffed back in, only to get wrinkled before the next wearing. Have you ever had a shirt professionally laundered, and then found it got so wrinkled in your closet you had to iron it to make it presentable? That circumstance will cause a bad case of laundry blues.

Exercise 77

Your thoughts: Fill in the chart below:

Housekeeping area I want to improve	Principles I can apply	End result I will enjoy when I do this

Chapter Twenty-Three: Cooking & Grocery Shopping

Let me describe to you, my's I Hate Cooking Method of Dealing with Cooking and Groceries. It is a simple system for dealing with the business of feeding a family. First off, I have to be honest: my husband does the real cooking in my house. He starts with a roux. I start with a can of condensed mushroom soup. When he cooks, I usually clean. When I cook, I also clean.

Because I am not a "natural" in the kitchen, it is easy for me to procrastinate on the tasks that would make kitchen life easier. Here's a master plan we have developed that results in having semi-nutritious meals four to six times a week.

Decide what to eat.

Make a list of complete meals that you know how to cook and your family will eat. Aim for six to ten meals to cycle through. When you create your list, think of things that will generate leftovers that can be eaten at least one more time. If there are dietary considerations, allow for them. It is also a good idea to follow the general rule about having multiple colors of fruits and vegetables in each meal. You want to try and create meals as healthful as your family will eat.

I'd also consider the preparation and cleanup time. This isn't just a one-week list, this is a family master list. You don't have to use it forever, and you should probably reevaluate it a couple of times a year.

Do adequate preparation.

From your master menu, create a master grocery list. It sounds like a silly suggestion, but trust me, if you take this next step, even your teenage son will be able to do most of your grocery shopping.

Before you shop.

You're going to index the grocery store. If your store provides a pretty detailed floor plan on an app that identifies where items are located on each aisle you might be able to skip this step, but if not, it is worth the time. Taking a clipboard, go up and down each grocery store aisle, one side at a time. You are looking for the name of every product your family uses on that aisle. If you don't use anchovy paste—don't write it down. But if your family uses ten other things nearby—write down all of them. I'd even indicate the brands if you are selective.

Do this up and down every aisle in the store. You now have a master grocery list of everything your family buys. If you want, type the list up. I just keep mine on large index cards, one per aisle, so I can flip through them easily. You can also use apps on your phone if you're not a physical copy person—personally, I think writing everything down with a pen and paper makes it stick in my brain a little more!

Take Inventory.

Now that you've gotten this master list, cross-check it against your menus. This step is the time to make sure when you shop you get every single item to create everything on your six to ten family-pleasing menus. No more half-made meatloaf only to go to the pantry to find no tomato paste.

Mark the items needed for your menus as "must have on hand items." You'll also want to mark other household essentials—bathroom tissue, soap and such. The idea is, if you always have these things in your freezer and pantry, you always have a meal ready to go.

Each week when you make up your grocery list, use this master list to create your weekly shopping list. In our house it is not uncommon for my husband to have his head in the pantry, with me calling out items while he yells back, "Green beans? Three cans!"

Then shop efficiently.

Things we need, I add to my list. When I am finished, I have a list of products to buy and it is in order that items are arranged in the grocery store. And now, post pandemic, we've all gotten hooked on grocery deliveries, this is even easier.

When it comes to deliveries, there is an added cost, true. But consider the cost of your time in the equation, and the trade-off is much better. Factor in impulse purchases you are not making, and (for me at least) delivery is a huge money saver.

This method doesn't solve the issue of having to actually cook the meals, but I have found the fewer decisions there are to make, and the more accessible the ingredients, the less of a chore cooking really is. And since I have created menus that generate leftovers, I try to have a "heat up" night in between every "cook" night.

It is also good to periodically declare war on stored food, both canned and frozen, to clean out your inventory. You don't want to stumble over cream corn from two years ago.

Make it a point to cook one bulk meal at least one day a week. By this I mean something that is just as easy to cook twenty servings as two. Chili and soup are good examples. So are casseroles to freeze. If you are making one batch of wild rice casserole, doubling the recipe is not much extra trouble at all. Freeze the extra for low stress meals on busy nights.

Give yourself a break too. If it works in your budget, go out to eat one night each week—or declare Sunday as "pizza" or "leftover" night and spend the time you would have spent cooking watching a family movie or playing a game. We've found a high-quality frozen pizza and a salad make a great movie night meal.

Exercise 78

Your thoughts: List five ways you can become more organized when it comes to meal planning

and preparation. Don't forget to declutter your fridge, pantry and counters.

Chapter Twenty-Four: How to Organize an Event

Organizing an event is a terrifying experience for some people. While it can be tedious, making an event happen—from a small seminar to a lavish event for 2,200 is just a matter of organizing the task.

Develop a mission statement.

I start any event planning with a mission statement. To craft an event mission statement, begin with the end product in mind. What do you want the event to be like? (You can ignore money for a minute while we hash out the details.) Is intimate and cozy more important than big and splashy? If you take anywhere from ten minutes to an hour to really think about what you want out of your event, you'll be in a good position to write a three or four sentence mission statement. Include others involved, if necessary. Create a picture of your "ideal" event. List the elements you feel are critical to the event's success.

Write this statement down. A written mission statement is a real mission statement. One you carry in your head is just the glimmer of an idea.

Now we analyze the mission statement. Is it realistic? If your budget is lemonade, don't plan for champagne. If champagne is the most important thing, then be ready to make cuts in other areas.

What are the other problems you see with your event? With the help of others involved, create a master list of "issues" that are in the way of your event. This stage is where you brainstorm and try to find out the weak point of your plan. Go ahead and write these down, as it is good to be mindful of them.

Now, with your list of potential problems, go back and adjust your mission statement accordingly. If space is an issue, reduce the size of the event, or find a bigger venue. If money is an issue, focus on the things that really matter and eliminate things that matter less. With this revised mission statement, you are ready to begin planning a detailed list of everything you need to do.

With your mission statement in front of you, make a list of everything that has to happen for the event to be created in accordance with your mission. This can be a stream of consciousness exercise. Try using 3x5 cards for this, since they can be shuffled. Put down all your wishes, hopes and dreams, too. We know that some aren't possible, but go ahead and put them down. This task may take several sessions, but try to make as comprehensive a list as you can, as it will be used to create your master plan.

Once you have all your "things that have to happen" in front of you, you probably see how overwhelming the task is. This is where we become very realistic. Delete everything from your "has to happen" list that can possibly be deleted!

About those "wishes" and "dreams" that were written down, pay attention to these and try to honor the ones that can be honored. For those that are simply not going to happen, it is better to write down the dream, and consciously delete it and mourn it than to have a glimmer of hope for it in the back of your mind, secretly complicating every decision.

From your remaining items, develop a timeline. Make it as detailed as possible and start as far out from the event as is realistic. Now that we've gotten the timeline, it may be that you see there is more than can be comfortably handled within the parameters you are operating. Once again, delete things that are unnecessary. (Now that you see how much there is to do, your standards may drop.)

Sit down with your timeline and your personal calendar and write everything on your timeline in the calendar. Take special notice of time crunches. You'll need to get help with these areas. You'll probably need to put a comprehensive timeline in the back of your calendar to consult from time to time when you need to review the big picture in addition to the tasks on your daily reminder list.

Next, look over the entries in your calendar and mark those that need advance notice to address. Flip a few days forward and give yourself advance notice. Now you have a master plan and calendar for your event. All you have to do is to get started.

Planning an Event: Thanksgiving Dinner Template

An event that nearly all of us have at some point in our lives is Thanksgiving. I have jotted down below my thoughts on getting ready for this event. My event will be small, not more than twenty people. Thus, the preparations are rather simple. This method can be used for a more complex event, too.

First, what has to happen between now and Thanksgiving morning? I try to think of everything I want done. (Some may get eliminated—like edging the sidewalk—but it is good to at least think about it, just in case time presents itself.)

Here are common tasks you might want to think about. You should create a deadline for each.

Task: Deadline:

Set Guest List   _____

Invite & confirm guests   _____

Set menu   _____

Make master grocery list   _____

Check to see what's on hand _____

Shop   _____

Buy wine   _____

Edge sidewalk   _____

Rake leaves   _____

Clean gutters (if time)   _____

Vacuum house   _____

Other housework:

_____   _____

_____   _____

_____   _____

Set table   _____

     Placemats Out   _____

     Decide on centerpiece, etc.   _____

Set up centerpiece   _____

     Napkins ironed and folded   _____

Set out cutlery   _____

Cook ahead anything possible:

     Dessert   _____

     Side dishes   _____

     Tea   _____

     Other   _____

     Other   _____

Make appetizer & punch   _____

Thaw turkey   (takes three days)

_____

Prep turkey in browning bag night before _____

I could add anything else in here that I want to attend to. Have the dogs washed and groomed, so they are smelling their best? I need to add it to the list. I try to put down every single thing I can think of.

Below there is a timeline for the day of the event. I make one of these up for almost any event, from a professional conference to a casual party. A timeline has several benefits.

One major advantage in writing down everything is that it shows you when you will have a time crunch. In the case of Thanksgiving, I know right off the bat that I need to use ready-made rolls. I have only one oven, so I need to plan for what hours the oven will be at what temperature. Desserts can be made the day before, which will relieve the burden on my single oven.

This timeline also tells me when I need to delegate, and when I need to simplify.

All of these things become apparent when you establish a time frame.

Timeline for day of event:

8:15	Turkey in oven
8:30	Make dressing
9:00	Set up coffeemaker
9:30	Prepare vegetables for steaming
9:40	Prepare vegetables for stovetop
10:00	Get out plates and glasses
10:30	Put sweet potatoes in oven
11:00	Put out appetizer & punch
11:15	Turkey out of oven to rest
11:15	Put dressing in oven
11:30	Make gravy (Bob)
11:30	Turn on vegetable steamer
11:30	Start stove top vegetables
11:40	Start microwave vegetables
11:45	Slice turkey (Cover and keep warm)
11:45	Rolls in oven
11:50	Ice in glasses
11:50	Sweet potatoes out of oven
11:50	Set up buffet line:

Turkey

Sweet potatoes

Misc. vegetables

Dressing

Gravy

Tea and water

11:55   Blessing

12:00   Begin buffet line

12:00   Turn on coffee maker

12:05   Pass rolls

1:00   Announce dessert

Having lists like this posted in your kitchen will help you delegate to "helpful" guests who insist on doing something, even when you've got it under control.

Exercise 79

Action step: Develop a mission statement and a timeline for a small event.

Hint: You might want to read my book, *Open Heart Open Home: Overcome Your Fear of Entertaining & Enjoy Warmer Relationships with Friends & Family.* In this book I delve very deeply into hospitality and event planning.

Chapter Twenty-Five: The Brain Dump

Have you ever had (what seemed like) forty things spinning around in your head, and just trying to keep track of them stressed you out? Or headed to the grocery store with a mental list of five items, only return without one of them? If so, a brain dump can be very helpful in reducing the brain cells you devote to needless tracking. You're going to make a list!

We've talked about your calendar and how important it is, but to maximize its use, you'll want a "Master List" to go along with it. What is a Master List? It is your most comprehensive list possible of all the things you and your family must attend to each year. And the best thing about this list (the result of your brain dump) is that it will help you reduce the static clogging up your brain as you struggle to remember things.

This wonderful list will include all your regular health appointments—from orthodontist visits to annual physicals. It will include your pet's vet check, too. You will put on this calendar everything you do seasonally—from pressure washing the deck in the spring to putting up storm windows in the fall. You won't put on it carpool duty, or weekly swimming lessons—these go in your calendar. You should, however, note the beginning and ending of swim season.

Here's how to create a master list.

Begin with ample blank paper. Label different sheets of paper with appropriate headings, such as Home

Maintenance, Health, Christmas, Vacation, plus any categories you need for work projects that occur annually.

Exercise 80

Action step: List your headings in the space below. Here are some suggestions. Think of as many as you can.

House Maintenance

Insurance Renewals

Yard Maintenance

Family Wellness Visits

Vacation

Annual Stressful Work Projects

Vet Visits for Pets

Church Events and Programs

Transfer these to individual sheets of paper or large index cards. Now you have your subject lists.

The next step will be to jot on each appropriate list everything you can think of that falls in that category. As you write, you'll think up whole new categories to add— just pull out a separate piece of paper. You may want to give yourself two or three sessions of brainstorming for this job. It is very much like planning an event—and you are! You are planning a year in your family's life.

Exercise 81

Action step: Begin doing this now. It might take several sessions for you to think of everything. It might help for you to go through previous years' calendars to remind you of annual or seasonal things you have scheduled in the past.

Once you've added everything you need to do in your life, you'll need to divide the tasks up by months. Most calendars are too small, so start with twelve sheets of notebook paper labeled for the months of the year and start with your first list and assign every task to a month.

Some tasks "belong" in certain months. But other things are more flexible. You might want to save the flexible tasks for last and see what months have the fewest tasks assigned to them and put those things in those months.

Exercise 82

Action step. Place every entry on your lists onto their appropriate months.

Now, once you've taken all your lists and divided them up into twelve months of tasks—get out a calendar. You'll need to write all your tasks down on a family master calendar. Many of the tasks will need to go on your personal calendar, too.

Exercise 83

Action step: Set aside time to add these to your calendar and to any other calendar that is not synched automatically.

Keep your twelve, monthly pages and don't throw away the pages of your family master calendar as the year goes by—instead keep both sets to use to create next year's master calendar.

When you do this, it will be instantly obvious if a new plan interferes with something scheduled on your master calendar. If your family vacation is in June, but that's also an opportunity for your son to go to summer camp, as soon as you flip to the page you'll see the potential conflict. Your calendar isn't set in stone and you can modify things. But keeping the master calendar in combination with your master to do list will help you avoid double-booking big commitments.

Exercise 84

Action step: Make a commitment to review your annual master calendar at least one a month. Enter that on your calendar do you do not forget.

Chapter Twenty-Six: Managing Your Priorities

A priority is merely a ranking you give to an item, giving it weight in the quest for your time and attention. The things you give attention to are your priorities, whether by your own conscious choice or by default from lack of planning. Here are some guidelines for managing your priorities.

1. Admit you can't do everything.

In a perfect world, there is adequate time for all the tasks you face each day. If you had adequate time, setting priorities would only be a matter of doing the items due first before addressing the items due later. But this is not a perfect world, even though some people prioritize only by "due date." By admitting that accomplishing everything is not only unlikely, but also perhaps impossible, you then become ready to actually make meaningful decisions about your priorities. As long as you keep telling yourself "I can do all of this if I work hard enough," you will have difficulty prioritizing. You may also drive yourself insane.

2. "Management" comes first.

Management issues usually cause more headache than other types of issues. What's a "management issue?" An example might be best to illustrate. For those of you ever involved in a personnel dispute, you understand the impact of a management issue on your productivity. One dysfunctional employee can cast a pall over a whole department. That's a management issue. If a management problem looms, taking your time and energy away from your primary objective, make sure that problem is solved as quickly as possible. It is better to spend the energy to deal with the management issue than to continue to let it drain your energy and the energy from an entire operation.

3. Address your fears.

Sometimes when a task is daunting, we procrastinate. Admit your fear, and then use procrastination-breaking behaviors to get going on the project. Break it into small pieces or steps, set outside accountability--whatever it takes to get moving on a task. In most cases dreading a task is worse than doing a task.

4. If in doubt, throw it out.

That could be the motto for this book, couldn't it? By "it" I mean, look at your To-Do list and decide to go ahead and delete those items that have been hanging around for months on end. It is better to admit you're never going to get the dog's teeth cleaned and drop it from the list rather than sighing over it every week.

If it is something that really can't be ignored—such as getting a new car inspection sticker—just do it. You can throw it off the list by simply doing it. But don't let an endless stream of inconsequential items clog your weekly planning. Get them done or give up on them.

5. Think geographic.

Sometimes your daily priorities will fall out around errands or some specific type of activity (such as a morning scheduled to be spent doing correspondence on the computer). Group similar activities together. If you're going to be on the computer for three hours anyway, go ahead and type up the minutes for that meeting, too.

If you are out on errands, think about your total route and how many places you can cover in a single trip. You may be able to clump trips together and take care of multiple items on your list. Think creatively, too. If you only need one grocery item, consider going to the smaller store next to the hardware store you plan to visit anyway. It may be a little more expensive at the smaller store, but when you factor in the convenience, it is probably cheaper in energy and time.

6. When faced with seemingly equally important items, try thinking negatively.

The question to ask here is "What is the greatest negative consequence of my not getting this done on time [or now]?" When two items appear equally important, this question can help you figure out which one comes with the greatest penalties for non-action.

Also factor in here non-tangible aspects of postponing something. If you put off re-working your closet and it aggravates you every single morning, that daily hassle may add up to big negative impact in terms of the quality of your life. Who wants to be aggravated every morning?

If you hate being out of shape, but can't seem to make exercise a priority, factor in all the daily self-criticism you face and its impact on how you feel about yourself. Stopping daily self-loathing might be a higher priority than "getting fit."

7. Decide to do it.

If an item is a high priority and you know it, just do it. Sometimes it is easy to get sidetracked onto activities we enjoy more, but discipline can help us stay focused.

And it goes without saying:

Do the most important things first. (These are the things most central to your mission.)

Start the tasks that involve other people first, because committees take longer.

Delegate with clear guidelines and due dates.

Achieve balance between your priorities. Don't let a single task paralyze your work on other tasks.

Exercise 85

Your thoughts: are there areas where determining priorities is difficult for you?

What are they?

Using the suggestions above, can you clarify your thinking?

Action step: Practice prioritizing by evaluating your daily plans and to do lists. Sort activities by priority.

Chapter Twenty-Seven: Getting What You Want (Revisit Your goals)

Organization requires action on our part. We have to do something. Even executives that can afford to hire (or can't afford not to hire) experts to help them become organized are left with required action. They have to keep themselves organized.

This point is where things can fall apart. It is one thing to experience the rush of energy that results from a newly organized workspace. But it is another thing entirely to dedicate a small portion of every jam-packed day to organization tasks, such as filing, sorting and tossing junk mail and using your calendar correctly instead of leaving appointments written on sticky notes.

The missing ingredient is discipline. We have to discipline ourselves to continue to do the small things that make us more organized. And it is self-discipline we are really talking about. Everyone has access to the same amount of self-discipline or self-control. 100%.

When we choose to put things away, write in our calendars, or toss junk mail we are making a deliberate choice. Consistently making the right choices results in a more organized life. Not all choices have to be perfect, of course. But the more right choices we make to "do it now" rather than later, or to decide to throw it out, rather than stack it up for future consideration—the more we will find ourselves organized and enjoying the peace that comes from living a more organized life.

Discipline sounds like a very negative word. We associate it with punishment, reprimands, and compliance to rules we didn't make and don't like. But the type of discipline we want here is not negative. Discipline in this area is simply a matter of getting what we want.

Do you want an orderly workspace in your office or kitchen? If you really want it, then a series of small actions that you choose to make daily will give you what you want. That's discipline. No one has beaten you with a stick to make you act in a certain way. You have decided that an orderly workspace is worth your time and effort.

By consciously deciding what you want in your life, you can then determine what steps are needed to get it. Taking the steps to get there is discipline. Getting what you want is the end result.

And getting what you want out of life is truly a great thing.

Exercise 86

Your thoughts: Using the Pareto Principle (80-20 rule) determine what areas in your "prime 20%" can be better organized"

Take some time to develop a plan to address
these areas.

Thank you for spending time with

Organize Your Life

Skills You Need to **Conquer** the Areas of **Chaos** in Your Life

I love to hear from readers! Please reach out to me at HelenWardDay@gmail.com and check out HelenWardDay.com for my latest books.

Your review of this book at Amazon or Good Reads means a lot to independent authors like me! Reviews are the only way we can get the algorithm to pull up our books. If this book has been helpful, I'd love a review.

Made in the USA
Monee, IL
16 May 2023

33849288R00142